Invertebrates of Wales:
a review of important sites and species

by Adrian Fowles

Published by
the Joint Nature Conservation Committee,
Monkstone House, City Road, Peterborough, PE1 1JY.
ISBN 1 873701 55 1

Typeset, printed and bound by The Charlesworth Group, Huddersfield, UK, 0484 517077

Foreword

This book is a pioneering attempt to present the case for recognising and conserving the invertebrates and their habitats of a substantial part of the British Isles. It aims to indicate to naturalists and landowners in Wales the richness of such creatures as insects, molluscs and spiders in their care. Although some of the richest invertebrate faunas occur in southern England, considerable regional diversity exists throughout Britain due to variation in climate, geology and land use. Even within Wales there are marked differences between the faunas of similar habitats in different parts of the country. In this book, the important features within each part of Wales are highlighted. The reader's attention is drawn to the most significant sites for invertebrate conservation.

Some of the groups of animals discussed here are well-known to many people and have been studied in some detail. Butterflies and moths, dragonflies, grasshoppers and bush crickets are widely appreciated. Their distributions and ecological requirements are largely understood. Other groups, such as beetles, flies and spiders, have been the province of specialists. This account attempts to show the significance of invertebrates generally in the natural history of Wales.

As well as appealing to the general naturalist, I hope that *The invertebrates of Wales* will inform and help all those who care for the countryside. Often in the past the choice of sites for conservation, and the nature of their management, have been biased towards plants and birds, sometimes exclusively so. The assumption has been that if the plant communities are conserved the invertebrates will inevitably prosper. Now we know that this is no longer a valid assumption and, although we do not know all of the answers to the problems invertebrates face, this book will help conservationists to ask some of the right questions.

Most of the sites described in the Regional accounts are well-known and will be familiar to most Welsh naturalists and other land managers. However, many of the important sites, and even habitats, will come as a surprise because such information has rarely been widely publicised by invertebrate zoologists. *The invertebrates of Wales* makes these details generally available for the first time and will, I hope, give many naturalists a new perspective on the Welsh countryside.

An important aspect of this book is the way in which it draws attention to the many instances where our knowledge is inadequate to meet the task of proper conservation of invertebrates in Wales. Similar surveys of other parts of Britain have been made by Adrian Fowles and he is, therefore, well qualified to take a broad view of the problems. I very much hope that this book will help all those involved in conservation and land management in Wales to provide a future for the rare and interesting invertebrates in their care.

Dr Malcolm Smith
Chief Ecologist, Countryside Council for Wales.

About the author

Adrian Fowles is the Invertebrate Ecologist for the Countryside Council for Wales, based in Bangor. He has studied invertebrates in Wales for fifteen years and has a particular interest in weevils and the invertebrate fauna of river shingle banks. Raising awareness amongst conservationists of the needs of invertebrates is one of his chief concerns and he was instrumental in the formation of the Dyfed Invertebrate Group. As editor of the Group's newsletter since its inception he has been involved with promoting an understanding of the importance of invertebrate conservation. He has published papers on a wide range of invertebrate groups, including the Lepidoptera, Coleoptera, Diptera and Araneae. The text of this book draws extensively on his knowledge of Welsh habitats and their invertebrate faunas.

Contents

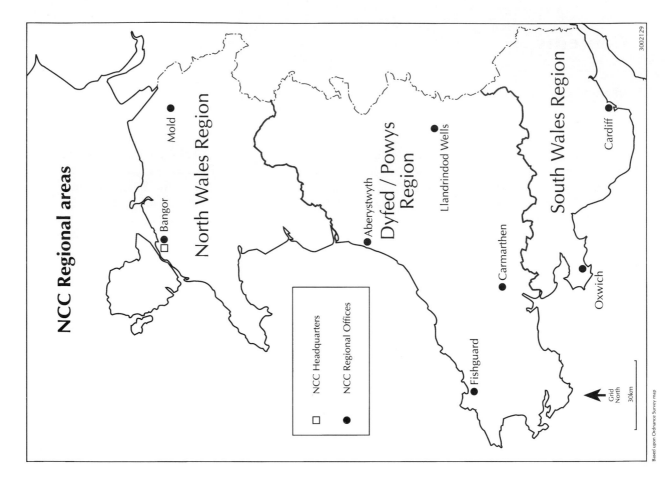

NCC Regional areas

North Wales Region

Mold ●
● Bangor
□

Dyfed / Powys Region

Aberystwyth ●

Llandrindod Wells ●

Carmarthen ●

Fishguard ●

South Wales Region

Cardiff ●

Oxwich ●

NCC Headquarters □
NCC Regional Offices ●

← Grid North
30km

Based upon Ordnance Survey map

3002129

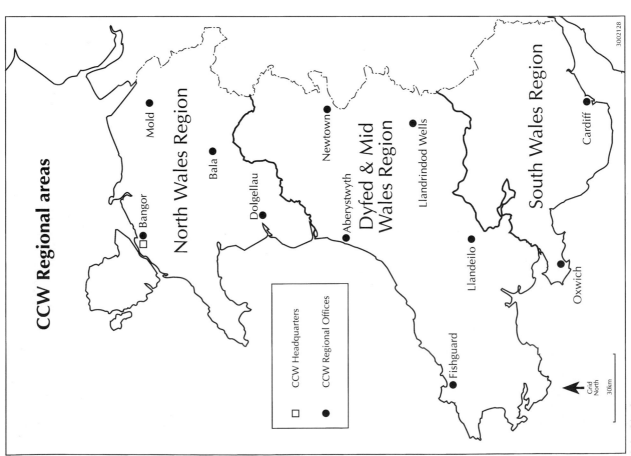

CCW Regional areas

North Wales Region

Mold ●
Bala ●
● Bangor
□
Dolgellau ●

Newtown ●

Aberystwyth ●

Dyfed & Mid Wales Region

Llandrindod Wells ●

Llandeilo ●

South Wales Region

Cardiff ●

Oxwich ●

Fishguard ●

CCW Headquarters □
CCW Regional Offices ●

← Grid North
30km

Based upon Ordnance Survey map

3002128

Introduction

Dyfed Invertebrate Group, Pen-yr-ergyd. [R.P. Bray]

Invertebrate zoologists have known for a long time that their objects of study have complex life-styles which are not necessarily catered for by the general principles of habitat management that have been historically adopted by conservation bodies. The widely-held belief that conserving plant communities will ensure the protection of invertebrate populations has been steadily modified in the light of ecological studies and there is now substantial evidence that many invertebrates respond dramatically to subtle changes in their environment. Much of this research has been carried out on butterflies but the lessons apply to a high proportion of the British fauna. Aspects of microclimate, habitat structure, management continuity and habitat juxtaposition are just some of the factors which are of critical importance for invertebrates. There is also an increasing recognition of the effects of habitat isolation on the extinction of invertebrate populations. With some 30,000 species in Britain

it is inevitable that invertebrates have narrower niches than the majority of higher plants and vertebrates. Habitat management has to reflect these diverse needs if we are to conserve the full ecological richness of our wild habitats. It is simply a question of scale and we must begin to recognise the intimate mixture of microhabitats within reserves and other valued sites, seeing more detail in the landscape than we did previously.

Invertebrates deserve our particular concern because they comprise by far the largest proportion of our native wildlife and because there are certain aspects of their life-histories which make them especially vulnerable to changes in the condition of their habitats. There are exceptions in all cases but, in general, there are five important principles to consider. (1) Many invertebrates require different conditions at different stages in their life-cycle. Larvae may develop in shady, moist environments, for instance, whilst adults of the same species need sunny, flower-rich habitats nearby to provide energy for egg-laying. (2) The short life-cycle of most invertebrates means that the correct balance of habitats has to be present each year without fail. A break in continuity will cause local extinctions of populations which may not be replenished in future years. (3) Many species have poor powers of dispersal and can neither escape catastrophic events nor readily re-colonise sites once favourable conditions are re-established. The increasing fragmentation of semi-natural habitats poses great threats to the less mobile species and makes the sensitive management of existing sites all the more important. (4) Current practice favours a middle-ground approach to habitat maintenance and invertebrates of the early and late stages of succession constitute a high proportion of the most threatened species. The pioneer communities of bare and sparsely-vegetated ground are in particular need of regular habitat management, whilst the invertebrates of over-mature timber are becoming increasingly restricted in distribution. (5) Invertebrates are very sensitive to climatic conditions, particularly temperature and humidity. Aspect, shelter, sunshine and shade exert a strong influence on which species inhabit different parts of a site. These features should be recognised as integral components of the habitat which are crucial for maintaining a stable microclimate.

In the past, the sheer number of species has hindered the progress of invertebrate conservation for all except a few of the most conspicuous insects. Which species are in need of attention? How many sites do they occur on? What specific measures do they require from conservationists? The answers to such questions are difficult to determine in most cases and hence invertebrates were often neglected in favour of other organisms, chiefly birds and higher plants, for which there was more reliable information. In recognition of these difficulties the Invertebrate Site Register was established by the Nature Conservancy Council in 1980. There was an obvious need to improve the position of invertebrates in the processes of site selection, defence and management by providing a clear statement on the faunas of individual sites with an indication of their national status and ecological requirements. Information was collated from a variety of published and unpublished sources, leading to the compilation of numerous reports which were circulated to relevant conservation organisations and invertebrate zoologists. Data pertaining to specific sites has been amalgamated into a series of county reports

covering the whole of Britain and national reviews of the status of invertebrates in a number of insect orders and some non-insect orders have been produced. New information is continually being collated, assessed and disseminated to a wider and wider audience. There is still much to be done to provide adequate answers to all of the questions facing invertebrate conservation but the situation has vastly improved. As the Invertebrate Site Register continues to gather data on the ecology and distribution of British invertebrates it becomes clearer that a high proportion of the fauna is declining through habitat loss and change. The issues of invertebrate conservation have to be more widely understood if this impoverishment is to be halted and, hopefully, reversed.

Conventionally, the Invertebrate Site Register (ISR) has dealt with non-marine species of macro-invertebrates and this review follows that approach. Our knowledge of the national status and habitat requirements of such groups as the Collembola or Acarini, for instance, is very limited and they are, as yet, not covered by the ISR. Assessment of the conservation status of marine invertebrates was regarded as the province of marine specialists within the Nature Conservancy Council and this information was maintained separately on a Marine Nature Conservation Review (MNCR) database. There is a degree of overlap with regard to intertidal faunas, however. Here, the convention has been that groups predominantly found in terrestrial or freshwater ecosystems, such as the insects, are included in the ISR whilst groups such as the copepods and amphipods that chiefly occur in marine environments are included in the MNCR. A few groups, notably the molluscs and isopods, are split between both the ISR and the MNCR. It is difficult to define a precise rule that governs this distinction, but in practice the allocation of a species to the marine or non-marine databases is usually fairly obvious. The scientific names of plants and animals are constantly being amended as understanding of our wildlife progresses. Whilst it is normal for natural history books to cite a reference work to the source of scientific names, in this case it has not been possible. The names used were current at the time of writing, and to conform to published checklists, where such exist, would be to adopt out-dated nomenclature. In a few cases, nomenclature has changed during the publication of *The invertebrates of Wales* and it has not been possible to update the text in all of these cases.

Whereas it is undoubtedly true that overall species-richness is at its greatest in southern England, chiefly due to climatic factors, it is also evident that other areas of Britain also contain nationally important sites or species as a result of regional variation in land use, geology, climate, or habitat distribution. This account of the invertebrates of Wales is an attempt to describe those particular aspects of the Principality which are of major significance for conservation. It is arranged in three separate sections, each of which corresponds to one of the Regions of Wales formerly administered by the Nature Conservancy Council, i.e. North Wales, Dyfed-Powys and South Wales. This arrangement of the text has necessitated some repetition but the overall intention has been to focus on those species, communities or microhabitats which exemplify the strengths, in invertebrate terms, of the individual Regions. Although it has only been possible to mention a fraction of the sites and species of interest, these have been selected to represent the salient features of invertebrate conservation in each Region. It is not necessary to document completely the fauna of a site before conservation is possible as an understanding of the basic principles is sufficient to allow a confident appraisal of invertebrate needs. There will always be scope for enhancing information on the distribution and ecology of invertebrates but we can no longer afford to hide behind a shield of ignorance. Habitat management, site protection, invertebrate surveys and ecological studies need to be initiated and sustained for the benefit of the rich invertebrate fauna of Wales. It is also essential that information continues to be submitted to the Invertebrate Site Register. The Joint Nature Conservation Committee and the Countryside Council for Wales owe a tremendous debt to the co-operation of invertebrate zoologists, both professional and amateur, and continuing support is necessary if the interests of invertebrates are to be adequately served by conservation organisations as a whole in the future.

North Wales: Notable sites for the conservation of invertebrates (see Appendix 1.)

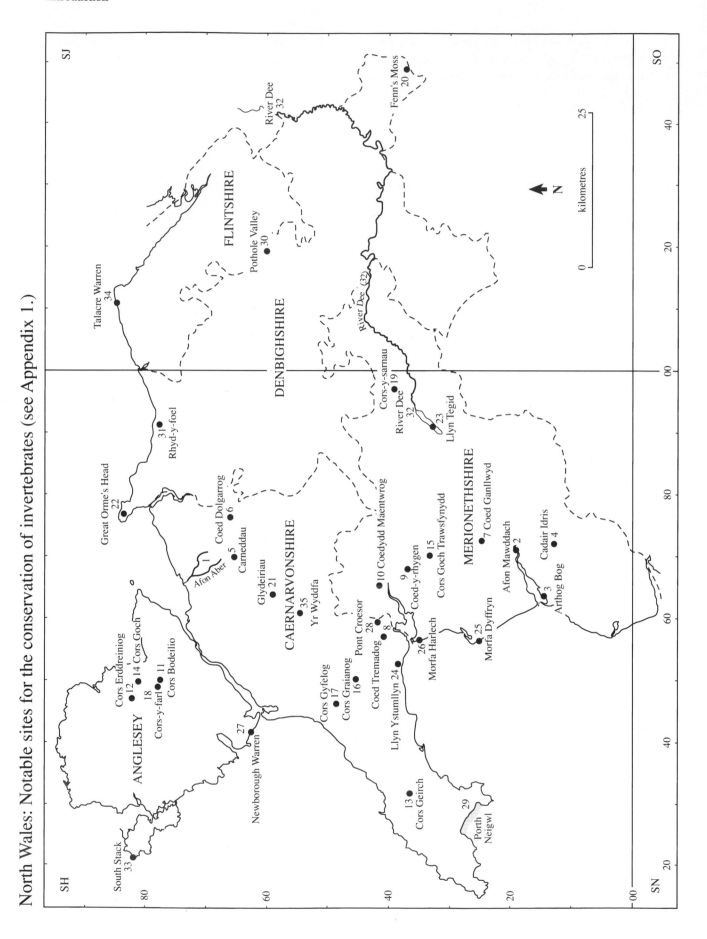

North Wales Region

Arans, Gwynedd. [R.P. Bray]

Introduction

The area covered by this review corresponds to the North Wales Region of the Countryside Council for Wales. This comprises the modern administrative counties of Gwynedd and Clwyd which, in biological recording terms, equates to the vice-counties of Merioneth, Caernarvon, Anglesey, Flint and Denbigh. The varied countryside of North Wales occupies an area of some 6200 square kilometres, of which more than a third is contained within the Snowdonia National Park. The population is mainly distributed along the eastern border, in towns such as Wrexham and Connah's Quay, and along the northern coast between Caernarfon and Prestatyn. These two concentrations are chiefly linked with the industrial zones of Deeside and Wrexham Maelor and the tourism belt of Prestatyn, Rhyl, Colwyn Bay, Llandudno, etc.

With the exception of a few small towns, the rest of the Region is largely rural in character with an essentially pastoral economy. Sheep and cattle grazing is the major land use, with commercial forestry accounting for a significant area of the uplands.

Geologically, North Wales is extremely interesting and complex. There has been considerable faulting and volcanic activity which has given rise to much of the spectacular topography of Snowdonia whilst the younger rocks of Clwyd have weathered to form a rolling landscape and more fertile soils. Ordovician rocks occur as a variety of sedimentary formations and account for the largest area of the Region. All of the major mountain blocks in Gwynedd, with the exception of the Rhinogau, are of Ordovician origin. It is a resistant rock, only slowly weathering to form poor, acidic soils but in many places there are richer igneous intrusions. The Rhinogau are situated in the middle of the Harlech Dome, a circular expression of older Cambrian sandstones, shales, mudstones and slates. Much of Anglesey and part of Lleyn is composed of Pre-Cambrian rocks and, where these are exposed along the coast, there are dramatic sea-cliffs. The country rock east of the Vale of Conwy is much younger and is dominated by Silurian shales and sandstones, forming the distinctive rounded hills of the Denbigh Moors for instance. Of major importance for wildlife in the Region is the presence of fairly extensive outcrops of Carboniferous Limestone on Anglesey and from Great Orme's Head south-eastwards across Clwyd towards Oswestry. Geological faults are responsible for the Malltraeth Trough on Anglesey, Llyn Tegid at Bala, and many other topographic features which are nowadays of great significance for nature conservation.

The high mountains of Snowdonia were a natural focus for glacier formation during the Ice Ages and the landscape bears innumerable scars from the moving ice. U-shaped valleys, cirques and corries were gouged from the country rock and mounds of debris were left behind as the glaciers retreated. Much of the lower-lying land of North Wales is masked by boulder-clay and morainic drift with blanket peat occupying extensive areas of the higher ground on shallow slopes, particularly to the south-east. Along the coast, blown sand forms the important dune systems of Merioneth, Anglesey, and the Point of Ayr. Fertile alluvium fills the Malltraeth Trough and the floodplains of the larger rivers. These Quaternary deposits dictate the basic types of habitats which, after centuries of modification by Man, now predominate in the Region's lowlands. In North Wales, geological and geomorphological events combine to produce the outstanding range of wildlife habitats in close proximity that is such a feature of the Region.

The major dune systems of North Wales are justifiably regarded highly for their invertebrate faunas. It is particularly the three west coast National Nature Reserves of Morfa Dyffryn, Morfa Harlech and Newborough Warren that are of prime interest but Talacre Warren at the mouth of the Dee is also a high quality site. There are many invertebrates of conservation importance on these dunes, the bee and wasp faunas are especially valued, and dune slack habitats are well-represented. The scarcer British invertebrates occurring on these dunes include the sandhill rustic *Luperina nickerlii gueneei*, the mining bee *Colletes cunicularius* and the carrion beetle *Hypocaccus rugiceps*. North Wales also has the

greatest extent of soft-rock cliff habitats in the Principality. These sandy exposures are nationally scarce and are known to support a range of specialised invertebrates. Although soft-rock cliffs are frequent on both coasts of the Lleyn Peninsula very little is known of the fauna. The rare ground beetle *Tachys micros* is present and it is possible that several of these sites are of national importance.

Coastal heath is a cliff-top habitat on the hard geology of much of Anglesey and Lleyn, the best example occurring on Holy Island at South Stack. Here there is a very large population of the silver-studded blue *Plebejus argus*, a butterfly which has declined alarmingly in Britain during the latter part of this century. On the limestone grasslands of Great Orme's Head, the silver-studded blue is represented by an endemic dwarf subspecies, *caernensis*, and the grayling butterfly *Hipparchia semele* also has a dwarf subspecies here, known as *thyone*. Great Orme is the best-known of the limestone grasslands of the Region and supports an exceptional Lepidoptera fauna along with many interesting beetles and other invertebrates. Isolated patches of unimproved limestone grassland occur elsewhere in both Gwynedd and Clwyd and together constitute the largest extent of this habitat type in Wales.

Neither the river systems nor the lakes of the Region are particularly well-recorded for invertebrates. A relict boreal fauna, including the pea mussel *Pisidium conventus* and the water beetle *Dytiscus lapponicus*, is known from some of the Snowdonia lakes whilst Anglesey's lowland freshwater bodies have a rich dragonfly fauna, including the hairy dragonfly *Brachytron pratense*. The presence of the medicinal leech *Hirudo medicinalis* in a few of the island's pools is another important feature. The Afon Dyfrdwy, or River Dee, is the largest and also the most significant river. In its middle reaches, the stonefly *Isogenus nubecula* has a strong population in its only confirmed site in Britain. This species is also rare in Europe. The channel of the Dee is little-modified for most of its length in Wales and its bankside habitats offer undisturbed conditions for a variety of aquatic and riparian invertebrates. Casual surveys have shown that some of the North Wales rivers support a rich shingle fauna with nationally uncommon beetles such as *Perileptus areolatus* and *Scopaeus gracilis*. Riverbank woodlands are well-distributed and important habitats for many Diptera with semi-aquatic larvae.

The oceanic sessile oakwoods of Snowdonia are outstanding for their bryophytes, lichens and fungi and are also of great interest for invertebrates that require sheltered, humid environments. Studies have shown that the craneflies and fungus gnats are characteristically rich in these woodlands and many nationally uncommon species thrive in abundance in the larger oakwoods, such as Coed Crafnant and Coedydd Maentwrog. The woodlands of Clwyd are generally less well-known but what information exists suggests that they support a different fauna which is more closely allied to lowland English woods than the western oakwoods of Gwynedd. The fauna of over-mature timber is also under-recorded in the Region but there is a wealth of old parklands that are of potential interest. There was a generally held opinion that western Britain had an impoverished saproxylic fauna but increasing knowledge is changing this view. There are certainly differences, as would be expected, between the invertebrate assemblages of southern English parks and Welsh parks but the latter have their own strengths and deserve greater recognition.

Peatlands are very much a strong point of nature conservation in North Wales and there are several outstanding sites of considerable invertebrate importance. Fenn's Moss, a raised mire complex on the Clwyd/Shropshire border, is one of the most famous entomological localities in Wales and a vast number of rare species has been recorded during this century. Commercial peat extraction in the recent past has damaged a high proportion of the mire surface but now that it is a National Nature Reserve there is ample opportunity to repair the damage. Fenn's Moss, along with the adjacent Whixall Moss in England, contains an excellent diversity of peatland moths, including the Manchester treble-bar *Carsia sororiata* and the northern footman *Eilema sericea*. The very rare caddisfly *Hagenella clathrata* is present in one of its few British sites and the jumping spider *Sitticus floricola* has recently been discovered here. In the past a number of rare peatland flies were recorded and modern surveys for many invertebrate groups would be of great value for future management.

On Anglesey and the Lleyn Peninsula there are several calcareous valley fens which are unparalleled in Wales. The National Nature Reserve of Cors Erddreiniog is a good example with a variety of rich fen plant communities and an interesting invertebrate fauna scattered throughout the site. Lime-rich seepages on the edge of the fen are of particular importance and are the breeding habitat, for instance, of the beautiful soldier fly *Stratiomys chamaeleon*. Nearby there is a small population of the southern damselfy *Coenagrion mercuriale* at its northernmost British locality.

Upland habitats dominate much of the Region and the large number of high altitude summits is without comparison in the rest of Wales. There are many boreal and arctic-alpine invertebrates which reach their southern limit within Britain on the mountains of Snowdonia and several of these are understandably scarce in national terms. Montane species of interest include the spider *Micaria alpina* and the rove beetle *Ocyusa hibernica*. Probably the most famous invertebrate of the Region's mountains is the rainbow leaf beetle *Chrysolina cerealis* which is known from a handful of localised populations on Snowdon and neighbouring mountains. The rainbow leaf beetle is legally protected as it occurs nowhere else in Britain and the strength of its populations is poorly known. The North Wales uplands are also home to two other insects which are effectively restricted to the Region, the Ashworth's rustic *Xestia ashworthii* and Weaver's wave *Idaea contiguaria* moths, both of which are widely distributed but local here. Blanket mire is well-developed in parts of the south and east, as on Migneint and Berwyn, and contains a characteristic acid peatland fauna. One speciality of this habitat is the ground beetle *Trechus rivularis*. Only recently discovered as an inhabitant of blanket mires, it was previously regarded as endangered in the few fens of eastern England that were considered to be its last refuge.

Such discoveries can still be made today in North Wales because the Region has shared in the historical neglect that invertebrates have experienced throughout the Principality. Historically there have been very few resident invertebrate zoologists and most of the early information on the Region's fauna was derived from visiting naturalists drawn to the wild countryside of Snowdonia. Their efforts were chiefly concentrated in two areas — the Barmouth to Harlech coastline and the mountainous habitats of Snowdon and Llangollen. Lepidoptera were the chief quarry for many of these early entomologists, who were attracted to North Wales in search of Weaver's wave, Ashworth's rustic and the Welsh clearwing *Synanthedon scoliaeformis*. The rainbow leaf beetle was obviously much sought after and specimens were displayed at many entomological exhibitions around the turn of the century. Morfa Harlech was a popular collecting site on the west coast and most naturalists concentrated on the dune systems. The Barmouth hills were also favoured and there are several accounts of high brown fritillaries *Argynnis adippe* in abundance here up to the 1950s and there were also unsubstantiated reports of large blues *Maculinea arion*. Newborough Warren on Anglesey, Great Orme's Head, and Fenn's Moss attracted many visiting lepidopterists but throughout the first half of this century there were few resident zoologists to widen the sphere of recording.

Members of the Lancashire and Cheshire Entomological Society had always maintained an interest in the North Wales fauna and during the late 1940s and 1950s several valuable papers were published in their 'Cheshire and North Wales Natural History' series. However, the modern era essentially began with the creation of an invertebrate data-base for the counties of North Wales by Mrs Joan Morgan at the University College in Bangor. Records collected from student projects and field meetings of the local Wildlife Trust provided the basis for this now extensive collection of data. Several field meetings bringing together national experts were instrumental in the 1970s for broadening knowledge of the strengths of the Region's invertebrate fauna. The Biological Recording Group for Wales, the Diptera Study Group, and a specialist survey of the top fenland sites, all revealed the importance of various habitats for a range of species and added many invertebrates to the known fauna.

Whilst there is still a need to collate survey data throughout the Region, in recent years there has been an increasing tendency to combine this with management-based studies. Four sites — South Stack, Newborough Warren, Coedydd Maentwrog and Rhinogau — have contributed to the Butterfly Monitoring Scheme, although only Newborough continues to provide transect data from North Wales. The Nature Conservancy Council's Welsh Peatland Invertebrate Survey was a major study that included forty-three sites in North Wales, fieldwork being carried out in 1988. Monitoring programmes have been established by the Countryside Council for Wales for the rainbow leaf beetle and the glutinous snail *Myxas glutinosa*, the first priority for the latter species being to determine whether it still occurs in Llyn Tegid. Invertebrate management is an acknowledged concern of the landowning conservation bodies in the Region and local naturalists mirror the growing national interest in popular insect groups. The recent formation of the Clwyd Entomological Society and the North Wales Invertebrate Group provides a focal point for developing an understanding of the importance of invertebrates in nature conservation and their particular requirements. Such initiatives need to be fostered if conservation is to have the knowledge and experience necessary to sustain the Region's rich fauna. It is a time for optimism but not complacency and the developing awareness of both the significance of invertebrates in habitat management, and the threats so many species face, should be strongly encouraged. There are many sites of national importance for invertebrate conservation and many species with national strongholds in the Region, embellishing the splendour of the North Wales countryside and deserving our continued attention into the future.

Coastlands

Bardsey, Gwynedd. [P. Hope Jones]

From the Dee estuary forming the border with England, westwards to Anglesey and then southwards around the Lleyn Peninsula to the Dyfi estuary, the North Wales coastline extends for some 400 kilometres. This is almost half of the total length of coast in Wales and it is therefore not surprising that coastal habitats are a major feature of the nature conservation interest of the Region. It is a narrow zone of immense variety, enhanced by the diverse geology and geomorphology encountered along its length, the differing aspects of its north, south and west-facing coastlines and the contrasting influence of sea conditions prevalent in the Irish Sea to the north and Cardigan Bay to the south. There are vast areas of tidal mudflats, numerous estuaries with sandy saltmarshes, rocky shores, shingle bars, lagoons, hard and soft-rock cliffs, and sand dunes. Each of these habitats has its own distinctive invertebrate fauna, adapted for survival in the frequently hostile world of the coastal fringe.

In common with most Regions in Britain, sand dunes have inevitably attracted most attention from invertebrate zoologists and several of the major dune systems are reasonably well-documented. Of the other coastal habitat types, such a statement can only be applied to the lagoons as they have been the subject of a recent survey commissioned by the Nature Conservancy Council. In fact there are only two true coastal lagoons in North Wales, a small pool in the shingle ridge at Aber Dysynni, Tywyn, and the twelve hectare lagoon behind the shingle spit at Cemlyn Bay, Anglesey. The Cemlyn lagoon was created in the 1930s by the construction of a small dam across its outflow channel but its brackish waters now support a high diversity of aquatic invertebrates, including the nationally scarce bryozoan *Conopeum seurati*. The level of information for the remaining coastal habitats is generally poor and there is much that can be done by local or visiting entomologists to help categorise the North Wales fauna and assess the quality and conservation value of different sites. It is clearly not feasible to have a comprehensive survey of all rocky shores, for instance, but increased recording would help identify the conservation needs of a particular habitat type and its likely importance in a national context.

Saltmarshes are a prime example of an entomologically-neglected habitat in the Region and yet, as they face continuing threats from development, invertebrate studies are needed to ensure that important sites are given the maximum protection. Pressures are most acute along the north coast where so much of the coastline has already been lost to industry, road building, tourism and residential developments. The saltmarshes of the Conwy have been severely damaged in past decades and it is not clear how much invertebrate interest remains. It is only at the mouth of the Dee around the Point of Ayr that we have some indication of invertebrate interest. Surveys of the saltmarsh Lepidoptera suggest that a reasonable fauna is present, including two scarce species of micro-moth, *Pediasia aridella* and *Coleophora adjunctella*. The saltmarshes of Anglesey and the Region's west coast are less threatened but *Spartina* is a constant worry and grazing by domestic stock can damage the saltmarsh fauna. The saltings of Traeth Melynog at Newborough Warren are the best known, supporting a similar assemblage of moths to the Point of Ayr and also an interesting beetle fauna. *Phaedon concinnus*, a nationally scarce leaf beetle which feeds on a range of plants in the upper saltmarsh, has been recorded and the ground beetles *Agonum nigrum*, *Dyschirius impunctipennis* and *D. politus* are also noteworthy inhabitants. Along the top of the Cefni saltings on the other side of the Newborough complex there is a strong population of the short-winged conehead *Conocephalus dorsalis*, almost at its northernmost limit in Britain.

Further south, there are substantial areas of saltmarsh on Traeth Bach (Morfa Harlech), Morfa Dyffryn, the Mawddach estuary, Broadwater, and the northern bank of the Dyfi estuary. The majority of this is grazed and hence stock should continue to be excluded from those areas where there is some control over management. The richest saltmarsh faunas are to be found on sites where the vegetational communities of the upper zone have not been modified by grazing. Here, plant-feeding beetles, moths, flies and bugs are at their most diverse and saltmarsh spiders and other predators benefit from the increased structural complexity of the habitat. The saltings at the north end of Morfa Dyffryn are a good example of a lush, ungrazed marsh, although they are practically unknown entomologically. Many of the saltmarsh invertebrates are more dependent upon substrate conditions than vegetation structure as they spend much of their lives inside burrows. Sediments containing a fair

proportion of sandy material are generally preferred as they drain well between tides and do not become anaerobic, unlike silts and clays. The banks of creeks often provide ideal conditions, harbouring species such as the rove beetle *Diglotta mersa* or members of the beetle genera *Bledius* and *Heterocerus*. Saltpans are another important feature, containing a small but distinctive community of water beetles. Recognition of these favoured aspects of the saltmarsh habitat can aid the detection of significant species and assist with the identification of potentially important sites. There will undoubtedly have been losses from the damaged saltmarshes of the north coast but there are still several sites in the Region where a rich fauna can be expected to occur and where invertebrate surveys could draw attention to localities of particular conservation importance.

Coastal cliffs, by contrast, face few direct threats and their invertebrates are generally widespread as their habitat, at least in western Britain, is extensive and largely undamaged. There are, however, a few aspects of concern to the invertebrate conservationist. Firstly it must be recognised that there are essentially two different types of coastal cliff, composed respectively of hard and soft rocks. Hard cliffs are formed from the Region's solid geology, the Ordovician, Cambrian, or Carboniferous rocks, for instance, that outcrop along so much of the North Wales coast. Invertebrates on the steep slopes of these cliffs inhabit stable substrates which are maintained by weathering and which are occasionally rejuvenated by local rock falls. Soft-rock cliffs are much scarcer and occur where there are thick coastal deposits of glacial till or other fine sediments. Their faunas occupy less stable habitats which are subjected to periodic erosion, creating slippages of bare sand and clay, a feature which is only represented to any extent in the Region along the coast of the Lleyn Peninsula.

It used to be a tradition nationwide to allow stock to graze on clifftop grasslands but this practice is now rare as fields have been improved up to the cliff edge and stock fenced out from the remaining fringe of unimproved heath or grassland. This has led to the majority of clifftop habitats becoming rank. As many coastal invertebrates are dependent upon bare soil for burrowing or hunting they have inevitably declined. Footpaths often offer the only suitable substrate in such habitats for bees and wasps, for instance. However, the oil beetle *Meloe proscarabaeus* (which is parasitic on solitary bees) has understandably declined as it is vulnerable to heavy trampling. Fortunately, choughs are

Whiteford Burrows, Gower: Peaty soils along a line of freshwater seepages on the transition between dune and saltmarsh support a number of scarce soldier flies and other Diptera with semi-aquatic larvae. (Photograph by A.P. Fowles.)

Taf Estuary, Dyfed: Saltmarshes with well-developed creek systems support a specialised invertebrate fauna which is adapted to cope with regular and prolonged periods of submersion. Burrowing species require aerobic sediments in sparsely-vegetated areas and the banks of creeks often provide suitable conditions. (Photograph by A.P. Fowles.)

Metrioptera roeselii **(Orthoptera):** The only known localities in Wales for Roesel's bush cricket are around the fringes of the Dyfi Estuary, where it inhabits brackish marshes that are occasionally flooded by the highest tides. (Photograph by S.G. Ball.)

Tywyn Burrows, Dyfed: Few dune systems in Wales include undisturbed strandlines in their succession as driftwood is eagerly sought for beach fires. Jetsam provides much needed shelter for many interesting species whilst others breed amongst piles of seaweed or in stranded timber.
(Photograph by A.P. Fowles.)

Talacre Warren, Clywd: Semi-stable foredunes are home to a specialised community of invertebrates that are adapted to this hostile environment. Trampling pressure from holidaymakers can deplete the fauna but on relatively undamaged stretches of foredune a surprising diversity of invertebrates can be found.
(Photograph by A.P. Fowles.)

***Vertigo angustior* (Mollusca):** This tiny snail is rare throughout Europe and one of its strongest populations is on Whiteford Burrows NNR, Gower, where more than a thousand snails per square metre can be found in suitable habitat.
(Photograph by D.G. Rands.)

Merthyr Mawr, Glamorgan: Herb-rich dune grassland and patches of bare, compacted sand are an ideal combination for nesting bees and wasps, many of which are becoming increasingly uncommon in Britain.
(Photograph by A.P. Fowles.)

evocative inhabitants of our coastal cliffs and their preference for grazed heaths and grasslands on which to search for their invertebrate prey is well known. Moderate levels of clifftop grazing on Lleyn, and elsewhere in Wales, for the benefit of choughs should also be of great value to cliff invertebrates.

A degree of trampling along coastal footpaths can be tolerated by the burrowing Hymenoptera and oil beetles but if public pressure is too great then the subsequent erosion can be very damaging. The popularity of Ynys Llanddwyn to holidaymakers has given cause for concern in the past as this is an important site for bees and wasps. Unregulated access must have affected many soil-nesting populations and as tracks widened and diverged even the rich fauna nesting in dead bramble stems came under threat. Solutions are not easy in such circumstances but on cliff footpaths, where space is available, the creation of alternative paths a few metres apart will help to reduce erosion and enhance the availability of nest-sites for burrowing species at the same time.

There is, of course, no need to create bare substrate by grazing or trampling on soft-rock cliffs as the inherent instability of the habitat ensures a continuous supply. The best soft-rock cliffs for invertebrates are those where there are numerous seepages and flushes as these can support a rich fauna of nationally scarce species, particularly amongst the beetles and flies. Certainly the most extensive, and quite probably the most important, soft-rock cliff site in Wales is Porth Neigwl at the tip of the Lleyn Peninsula. This is exposed to the southwesterly winds and much of it is too unstable for most invertebrates but, towards the western end, there is a lengthy stretch of valuable habitat in which slippages alternate with richly vegetated areas, small fens develop in the hollows formed behind landslips, and several shallow flushes run across the sandy slopes. It is only recently that the entomological significance of Porth Neigwl has been recognised but already surveys have shown that a characteristic fauna is present. The most interesting species recorded so far is the ground beetle *Tachys micros* at its only known site in Wales. Elsewhere this rare beetle has only been found along the south coast of England, where soft-rock cliffs are not uncommon. The occurrence of *Tachys micros* at Porth Neigwl suggests that, despite its geographical isolation this site can support a significant soft-rock fauna. The beetle *Eubria palustris* favours shallow seepages on soft-rock cliffs and base-rich flushes in fens. It is known from very few sites nationally

and its recent discovery at Porth Neigwl is a further indication of the significance of this site.

Although Porth Neigwl is the largest example, there are many other soft-rock cliff localities along the Lleyn coast which are as yet almost entirely unexplored. The most favourable sites will be along the south coast as aspect can be a crucial factor, but there are many good examples of the habitat along the north coast which should not be ignored. Porth Oer, for instance, has numerous calcareous seepages trickling down its sandy cliffs and these can support a valuable assemblage of flies with larvae that breed in mossy runnels and damp sediments, such as the soldier flies, craneflies, or dolichopodids. It is likely that many interesting discoveries will be generated in the future by surveys of the soft-rock cliffs of the Lleyn peninsula. In the meantime, we should seek to conserve the habitats by ensuring that natural erosion processes are not hindered or exacerbated and that the hydrology of the flush systems is neither impeded nor polluted.

The nature conservation value of sand dunes is much more readily appreciated and the many fine systems around the North Wales coast have drawn entomologists to sample their riches for the past century and more. Newborough Warren and Morfa Harlech, in particular, are amongst the best recorded invertebrate sites in the Region and this recording effort has demonstrated their national importance for invertebrate conservation. This does lead to an element of 'honeypot' recording, however, in that some of the other dune systems are ignored by visiting entomologists in favour of these more famous sites. It would be useful to try and direct future surveys to Morfa Dyffryn, Tywyn Aberffraw or Talacre Warren, for example, as these are all high quality sites where more detailed invertebrate information would be of great interest. Other dune areas on Anglesey, Lleyn and further south appear to be of lesser interest, chiefly due to high tourist pressures, although each will support some of the more notable dune invertebrates.

Newborough Warren is an outstanding site by any standard and more invertebrate records are available here than for any other individual site in the North Wales Region. Not surprisingly, a large number of nationally rare species have been recorded and Newborough is considered to be amongst the top national sites for the conservation of a wide range of invertebrate orders. One of the groups for which the larger Welsh dunes appear particularly important is the sand-nesting bees and wasps. It is now widely acknowledged that our aculeate Hymenoptera

Dark green fritillary *Argynnis aglaja*. [A.P. Fowles]

have declined markedly over the past forty years or so through widespread habitat loss or degradation. Most bees and wasps nest in sunny situations with a sandy or friable soil to facilitate burrowing. These conditions are obviously typical of sand dunes and a large and diverse fauna can occur on the better sites. Inland, suitable habitat is now scarce as agricultural improvement and urban expansion have claimed once-favourable heaths, commons and grasslands. On the dunes themselves, increased and uncontrolled public access has damaged areas of firm sand that formerly held large aculeate populations.

At other sites the decline of rabbits through myxomatosis allowed vegetation to heal over bare scrapes and eventually become too dense for nesting aculeates. Several of the Welsh dune systems, like Newborough, are large enough to withstand controlled public pressure and it is becoming increasingly apparent that their aculeate faunas are of national significance. The spider-hunting wasp *Arachnospila wesmaeli*, the solitary wasps *Oxybelus argentatus* and *Psen littoralis*, and the mining bee *Colletes cunicularius* are amongst the more notable species recorded from Newborough. *C. cunicularius* is found only on the dunes of Wales and north-west England and is a speciality of the Region. It nests in the south-facing slopes of semi-consolidated dunes and seems to feed entirely from the catkins of creeping willow. *Psen littoralis* is also typically found nesting in the early stages of dune succession and hence both species are particularly vulnerable to trampling damage on popular holiday beaches. Most bees and wasps, however, nest in firmer sand on the stabilised dunes where small-scale erosion, from rabbits, people or grazing stock, maintains open patches

for them to nest in. A rich fauna of aculeates on dune systems is generally indicative of a healthy site for dune invertebrates overall as the necessary mosaic of bare sand and flower-rich areas is also required by a wide range of other species. The robber fly *Pamponerus germanicus*, which is common at Newborough, hunts for its insect prey amongst sheltered sandy hollows. Most of its British populations now occur on Welsh dunes. Ground beetles are another important group in such habitats and scarce species recorded at Newborough include *Amara fulva* and *A. praetermissa*. Where there is damp sand, as at the edge of permanent or temporary pools in dune slacks, *Dyschirius* species prey on *Bledius* rove beetles in their tiny burrows. Spiders found only on dune systems include *Mecopisthes peusi*, *Ceratinopsis romana* and *Zelotes electus*, along with the more widely-distributed, and beautifully camouflaged, wolf spider *Arctosa perita*.

There are two major dune systems along the Merioneth coast, Morfa Harlech and Morfa Dyffryn, both of which have many species and habitat features in common with Newborough Warren. Both sites, however, have a better representation of embryo and fore dune habitats, particularly following a series of winter storms which, since 1974, have caused dune erosion along the south-west facing coast of Anglesey. Fore dunes are only capable of supporting a relatively small fauna that is adapted for life amongst the shifting sand but this includes several scarce moths. Species such as the shore wainscot *Mythimna litoralis*, the sand dart *Agrotis ripae* and the white colon *Sideridis albicolon* are all recorded from Morfa Dyffryn but have few other populations in North Wales. Another inhabitant of the fore dunes is the handsome tiger beetle *Cicindela maritima*, known from both of the Merioneth sites. It is an uncommon species nationally and, like the aculeates mentioned above, probably cannot withstand too much disturbance to its habitat and is restricted to the larger dune systems where visitor pressure away from access points is slight. This situation is convincingly demonstrated at Morfa Harlech where the fore dunes near the main beach access have little insect life but further away they become alive with a rich and valuable fauna. Searching dune hollows here on warm, windy days is a profitable way to record some of the rarer beetles as they get blown into depressions and cannot climb up on the loose sandy sides. A speciality of the Welsh dunes, the carrion beetle *Hypocaccus rugiceps*, can frequently be found by this technique and many other inconspicuous or elusive beetles are also trapped on favourable days.

Morfa Harlech is an exceptional site and invertebrate surveys there have really only hinted at the riches it contains; much more remains to be discovered. Whilst it has a good representation of dune ridge features, its most important aspects are probably the vast area of old dune grassland and the huge dune slack on its landward side. The cattle-grazed, sandy pasture is by far the most extensive example in Wales and it must surely have an interesting associated fauna. Unfortunately, records for the site are not sufficiently localised to categorise the fauna at present and it would be very useful to carry out detailed surveys to demonstrate the effects of grazing on dune invertebrates. The different micro-climate from that of ungrazed dune grassland should be beneficial to a host of warmth-loving invertebrates and areas of 'poached' turf damaged by trampling will provide ideal oviposition sites for beetles and flies with larvae that develop in sandy soil. Nationally, the fauna associated with dung on sandy soil includes several species which are now extremely rare in Britain as a result of the decline in the practice of grazing stock on dunes and it would be worthwhile investigating this aspect in the future.

The main slack at Morfa Harlech is very impressive. This large sheet of shallow water, surrounded by willow carr and iris beds, dwindles away from early summer to leave damp slacks with a rich flora and thickets of creeping willow. This provides perfect conditions for snail-killing flies, their larvae predating wetland snails that are stranded by the falling water-table. Morfa Harlech, like Newborough Warren, has a varied assemblage of these flies, including nationally

scarce species such as *Pteromicra glabricula*, *Pherbellia grisescens* and *P. griseola*. The rather local ephydrid *Ochthera mantis*, a curious fly with enlarged front femora, also occurs around the muddy margins of this slack. The bushes of creeping willow are host to the leaf beetle *Chrysomela populi* and the scarce bug *Monosynamma sabulicola*, whilst the catkins are visited by the hoverfly *Eumerus sabulonum* and numerous sand dune bees. The Welsh dunes are noted for their dune slacks, both for their flora and fauna, and Morfa Harlech's slacks are certainly of considerable importance.

Dunes along the north coast of Wales have suffered greatly and, although the belted beauty moth *Lycia zonaria* persists in one of its few British sites at the mouth of the Conwy on dunes which have been turned into a golf course, it is only between Gronant and Talacre at the mouth of the Dee that an intact dune system survives. Occurring here, and at a few other sites in Lancashire and North Wales, is the race *gueneei* of the sandhill rustic moth *Luperina nickerlii*, which feeds on sand couch as a larva. The moths of Talacre Warren are well documented and this is an important locality for dune and saltmarsh species, enhanced by the rich variety of the flora in this very interesting site. Although Talacre is a long and narrow system which is very popular with holidaymakers, it has a fascinating diversity of habitats and tourist pressure is localised. At least in terms of the Invertebrate Site Register, there is virtually no invertebrate information apart from Lepidoptera records and entomologists working on other groups could make a valuable contribution through future surveys. The highly localised weevil *Apion dissimile* has been found on hare's-foot clover in the dune grassland and other scarce invertebrates must surely await discovery.

To complete this introduction to the coastal habitats of the Region mention must be made of the clusters of islands off the coast of Anglesey and at the tip of the Lleyn Peninsula. Of course, Anglesey itself is the largest island but it is so close to the mainland that its habitats and fauna are hardly affected by isolation. Most of the offshore islands are little more than barren rocks whose chief interest to the invertebrate zoologist lies in the impoverishment of the fauna through exposure and isolation. Several of these have sizeable seabird colonies which will have their attendant invertebrates living on carrion or inhabiting nests. A few, such as the St Tudwal's Islands and Puffin Island, are perhaps large enough to support a reasonable selection of cliff grassland invertebrates but they are unlikely to be of any particular significance for conservation.

Bardsey alone is sufficiently large to contain a substantial fauna and it has attracted entomologists in a similar manner to Skokholm and Skomer off the Pembrokeshire coast. Over the years the species lists for the island have slowly grown and recently there have been attempts to investigate the ecological preferences of some of the resident species. Pitfall trapping, for instance, has shown how localised some of the ground beetles can be, even the limited wetland habitats on the island supporting nationally uncommon species such as *Pterostichus gracilis*. *Amara fulva*, quite a rare beetle in Britain as a whole, is found on the one small patch of dry sand on Bardsey. Comparatively simple ecosystems like this offer plenty of opportunities for detailed studies and there is considerable interest in the evolution of island morphs amongst animal species. The grayling butterfly *Hipparchia semele* on Bardsey has significantly shorter wings than its mainland neighbours and no doubt there are other examples to be found of species which have undergone adaptations to their exposed environment.

This selective account of the significant sites and habitats of the North Wales coast cannot do justice to the full range and quality that the Region has to offer. The important sites of South Stack and Great Orme will be discussed in the Heaths and Grasslands chapter, whilst others have had to be omitted through lack of space. Nonetheless, it is hoped that this brief summary conveys a flavour of the important features of the Region's coast and the undeniable wealth of its invertebrate fauna.

Woodlands

Coedydd Maentwrog, Gwynedd. [A.P. Fowles]

Scattered across North Wales, chiefly in low-lying districts, are a number of parklands associated with the larger estates and stately homes of the Region. These were mainly established in the eighteenth century when estate owners landscaped their grounds for amenity and other purposes and planted a variety of tree species to enhance existing native stock. On estates where these trees have survived the demand for timber over the past couple of centuries, conditions for wildlife exist which are now extremely scarce in our native woods. These trees are of an age where natural decay and storm damage produce micro-habitats of immense importance for a group of invertebrates which are collectively known as the saproxylic fauna. This term relates to those species which are dependent on dead or dying timber and the various phases of its subsequent decay, such as red-rot, the fruiting bodies of fungi, or the debris which collects in rot holes. Birch trees, for example, usually die when they are about eighty years old and hence develop saproxylic micro-habitats at a comparatively early age. Oaks and beeches, on

the other hand, may live for five hundred years and more and it is really only when they are about 200 years old that conditions which support some of the scarcer elements of the woodland fauna begin to be created. As old trees have been cut down in woodlands across Europe there has been an increasing decline in populations of saproxylic invertebrates and many interesting and attractive species have sadly become extinct.

In many parts of Britain today it is only in parklands that old trees have escaped the axe or the chainsaw and a relict 'old forest' fauna has survived. This has not always been evident to conservationists and there has been a tendency to regard parklands, with their artificial character and patchy canopy, as poor substitutes for the native deciduous woodlands. There is, of course, a large degree of truth in this as parklands cannot sustain the myriad species of plants and animals that inhabit semi-natural woodlands. Nonetheless, they now represent a last refuge for an aspect of our woodland heritage that contains some of the rarest and most threatened species of

British wildlife. This neglect is compounded by the fact that so many of the saproxylic invertebrates are inconspicuous and require a specialist both to find them and subsequently identify them. Fortunately, old trees are also valued for their rich lichen flora, another province of the specialist but at least one that is visible and readily demonstrated. Young oak trees have an acidic bark but as they grow older the acidity leaches out and the alkaline bark of ancient oaks is more suitable for the establishment of epiphytic lichens. In areas with low levels of airborne pollution, therefore, the presence of valued assemblages of ancient woodland lichens can serve as an indicator of good habitats for saproxylic invertebrates.

Beetles are one of the most important groups of invertebrates dependent upon the micro-habitats of over-mature trees but, unfortunately, there have been very few resident coleopterists in North Wales and beetle records are generally sparse. However, a few parkland sites have been surveyed briefly by visiting entomologists and there are indications that, despite the history of woodland management in the Region, a surprisingly rich fauna still survives. An example of this is Plas Talgarth in the Dyfi valley, an area of scattered old oaks on the edge of the estuary which was visited for one day in 1968. Species recorded here included *Orchesia minor, O. undulata, Bitoma crenata, Leptura sexguttata* and *Platypus cylindrus*. All of these are saproxylic beetles which collectively are indicative of a site of high conservation value. No further work seems to have been done on the saproxylic fauna of Plas Talgarth, however, and as there have been a number of developments in the grounds since 1968, it is not clear how many of the

ancient trees are still standing. At Rug, near Corwen, ancient roadside trees have produced specimens of *Pediacus dermestoides, Rhizophagus nitidulus* and *Xyloterus signatus*, scarce saproxylic beetles that are regarded as characteristic components of the old forest fauna that is now generally so rare. However, Rug has never been surveyed properly and the fine old oaks in the heart of the park could support an extremely important fauna.

Rug and Talgarth are two more or less random examples and there are many other fine parklands in North Wales which need to be comprehensively surveyed. Erddig near Wrexham, for instance, is known to contain a population of the very handsome black-headed cardinal beetle *Pyrochroa coccinea* and Baron Hill on Anglesey has the weevil *Mesites tardii* breeding in its old oaks. Surveys are required not just to enhance our knowledge of the fauna but also to ensure its long-term conservation. There is a continuing desire to keep parklands tidy; the practice of cutting up and burning fallen logs and removing dead branches from standing trees is still prevalent despite changing attitudes. With an awareness of the real or potential importance of a site for nature conservation these issues can be addressed and alternative solutions, where necessary, proposed. Without such knowledge further attrition of the fauna is inevitable. Over the next century many woodland trees are going to develop to maturity and there should be a parallel resurgence in the fortunes of the saproxylic fauna, building in a missing dimension to woodland ecology. This will only happen, however, if we manage to retain a network of 'old forest' refuges across the country to act as reservoirs of recolonisation in the future.

Black-headed cardinal beetle
Pyrochroa coccinea. [S.G. Ball]

Saproxylic invertebrates are notoriously slow at occupying new habitats and the process of revitalising the late successional stages of our native woodlands may take many hundreds of years, but we have to make sure those opportunities are available.

At present, the only woodland site known to support a representative saproxylic fauna is on the limestone slopes of the Alun valley in Clwyd. Here ash, elm and beech trees of considerable age have yielded an interesting collection of beetles which includes *Sinodendron cylindricum*, *Phloiophilus edwardsi*, *Colon dentipes*, *Dasytes plumbeus*, *Endomychus coccineus*, *Soronia grisea* and *Mycetophagus atomarius*. Although beech is not native to North Wales it can harbour an important fauna when it becomes a mature tree. This is because a high proportion of saproxylic invertebrates are more dependent upon a particular type of decay than upon the species of tree itself. Beech, for instance, often supports a wealth of fungi and a great variety of beetles and flies, and their attendant parasites, breed in the fruiting bodies of tree fungi.

Beech is also very prone to forming rot holes, cavities in the trunk or larger boughs where organic debris rapidly builds up and offers a rich medium for the development of fly larvae and a few specialist beetles. As with sycamore, which also has its good points when over-mature, the suppression of native woodland communities by invasive beech should be resisted but there is also good reason to retain venerable examples where possible.

Information on other invertebrate groups in the Region's parklands is even more lacking than that for beetles, although some sites do contain the solitary wasps *Ectemnius cavifrons* and *Crossocerus cetratus* which nest in dead trees in sunny situations, usually utilising old beetle burrows. Apart from the Coleoptera and the aculeate Hymenoptera, the other order of major significance in saproxylic habitats is the Diptera. In general, although there are undoubtedly exceptions, fly larvae require micro-sites with a high degree of humidity and this will tend to limit the fauna occurring in the open situations of landscaped parks. Some species will inhabit water-filled rot holes or even breed in sap runs on the tree trunk but most will prefer a degree of shade to prevent desiccation of the timber. A few fly families are particularly suited to permanently humid conditions and for them the 'Oceanic' oakwoods of Snowdonia are ideal.

North Wales has ten woodland National Nature Reserves, more than any other Region in Britain, and the chief reason behind the declaration of most of them has been to conserve their internationally important assemblages of lower plants: the bryophytes, ferns, lichens and fungi. The Region is favoured with so many good examples of this type of woodland primarily because of its geography and topography, resulting in a particularly suitable climate for the growth of such moisture-loving species. Warm Atlantic winds deposit their burden of rain on reaching the high ground of Snowdonia, saturating the woodland floor and strongly influencing the plant communities that thrive there. As with so much of Wales, ancient woodlands tend to have survived on the steeper slopes that have evaded the plough and which have grown back as coppice after periodic fellings. These valleyside oakwoods maintain a comparatively stable micro-climate with high humidity levels and surveys have shown that they contain a rich diversity of craneflies and fungus gnats.

The life-histories of these flies vary tremendously but a common factor is their dependence upon the prolonged wetness of their woodland habitats. The larvae of many of the uncommon craneflies of the Region, for instance, develop in wet soil or moss. Examples include *Tipula nubeculosa*, *T. yerburyi*, *Molophilus corniger*, *Diogma glabrata* and *Paradelphomyia fuscula*. *Lipsothrix errans* probably breeds in wet, rotten timber whilst small boggy mires, often a component of these woodlands, may have *Tipula holoptera*, *Triogma trisulcata* or *Limonia distendens*. The scarce cranefly *Limonia inusta* breeds in fungi so it is not surprising that it has been recorded at Coed Tremadog, one of the most productive sites for fungus gnats in recent surveys. The North Wales woodlands appear to be an important area for fungus gnats, a factor which must relate directly to their humid nature. Although some species are predators in rotten wood or feed on fungal mycelia, most develop inside fruiting bodies and are hence reliant upon the regular appearance of their short-lived micro-habitat. As fungi are somewhat unpredictable, it is only in the larger woods that a suitable food supply can be guaranteed for some of the more host-specific species. The British distribution of many fungus gnats is insufficiently known at present for us to be confident about their conservation status. It is clear, however, that woods such as Dolbebin and Coed Crafnant on the western flanks of the Rhinogau, Coedydd Maentwrog in the Vale of Ffestiniog, and Coed Tremadog above the Glaslyn floodplain, support an important diversity of fungus gnats, several of which have been recorded on very few occasions in Britain. Amongst those currently considered to be of Red Data Book status are *Anatella dampfi*, *Exechia sororcula* and *Phronia egregia*. Molluscs are another group that do well in the oceanic oakwoods, flushes and leaf litter harbouring 'ancient woodland' species such as *Leiostyla anglica*, *Spermodea lamellata* and *Zenobiella subrufescens* whilst the slug *Limax cinereoniger* tends to favour drier conditions, often under fallen timber.

The character of these damp and shady western oakwoods of Snowdonia is very different from the drier, more lowland, types of woodland occurring in the Vale of Conwy and eastern Clwyd. Their richer soils and lower rainfall promote a greater diversity of herbs in the ground flora and the shrub layer is often more varied, including spindle and purging buckthorn for instance. The sunnier, more open, woods are better suited to a range of plant-feeding insects which are either scarce or absent further west. Pearl-bordered fritillaries *Boloria euphrosyne* still occur locally, although they have declined dramatically over the rest of Wales, and grizzled skippers *Pyrgus malvae* and brimstones *Gonepteryx rhamni* are found in woods on base-rich soils. The high brown fritillary *Argynnis adippe* has been reported on several occasions in recent times from these eastern woods but no definite colonies have been confirmed. Current research indicates that the high brown fritillary breeds in sunny, but sheltered, bracken-filled glades, where eggs are deposited in deep litter. In such conditions there can be a profusion of violets in spring, on which the caterpillars feed. The decline of this magnificent, and now extremely rare, butterfly is probably linked with woodland neglect which has allowed glades to become scrubbed over. Certainly the urge to plant trees on sunny bracken slopes in woods where there have been comparatively recent sightings should be strongly resisted.

There is some evidence amongst the fauna that these lowland woods provide habitats for many insects which are generally rare in Wales but more widespread in England. The weevil *Apion pallipes*, which feeds on dog's mercury, is a typical example. Woodland moths are the best recorded group in this area and species such as the brown scallop *Philereme vetulata*, pale eggar *Trichiura crataegi* and the figure of eight moth *Diloba caeruleocephala* further demonstrate this phenomenon. The micro-moth *Agonopterix astrantiae* has been recorded on the Carboniferous Limestone of the Clwydian Range. This is a scarce, but probably under-recorded, species whose larvae feed on sanicle. The richer flora of the limestone woods undoubtedly accounts for some of the differences in the fauna but there are probably also climatic reasons involved. The

hillside oakwoods on the predominantly Silurian rocks of the Vale of Conwy are known to support interesting assemblages of southern woodland moths, presumably as a result of the favourable climate in the shelter of Snowdonia.

Continuing research into the ecology of individual plant-feeding species of invertebrates has shown that ground temperatures are often critical for successful breeding. New information is continually being presented which indicates the allegiances of woodland butterflies to foodplants growing in specific situations. Wood-edge violets may support up to five species of fritillaries but each species will require a different configuration of soil temperature, shade, and surrounding vegetation structure. Although such research is lacking for most phytophagous insects, it can be inferred that the weevils, plant bugs, leaf-mining flies, etc. will also contain species with similar demands. We cannot control the weather but we can cater for wood-edge invertebrates by maintaining and creating rides and glades in suitable stretches of woodland.

Native woods account for less than 5% of the total surface area of North Wales and many sites are either too small to be of significant conservation interest or have little long-term future because of a lack of regeneration due to sheep-grazing. These problems are being addressed and the position should steadily improve but there is still a need to identify the features of importance for invertebrate conservation and to ensure that those features are managed and conserved. There may be little to do in the oceanic oakwoods other than the arduous estate-work of fence repairs and scrub control in boggy glades. Elsewhere, small-scale coppicing and glade creation can help to enhance the woodland fauna. Wider recognition of the potential value of parklands for the saproxylic fauna must be a priority and some of these sites will need additional trees to provide some continuity for the future. Greater involvement by invertebrate zoologists in woodland surveys is essential if these conservation activities are to be based on sound information. Recently the Welsh clearwing *Synanthedon scoliaeformis* was rediscovered in Snowdonia after it had been presumed to be extinct in Wales for more than one hundred years. This nationally rare moth breeds in the trunks of living, mature birch trees and it is hoped that it still occurs in more localities than its current known site. However, to maintain a population of Welsh clearwings there will need to be sustained birch regeneration as the trees have a relatively short life span. Presumably other colonies have become extinct when this cycle has been broken or surrounding habitats have become unsuitable through agricultural improvement or afforestation. In the wooded habitats of North Wales there may be many more species of invertebrate that face local extinction because of a lack of understanding of their needs or knowledge of their presence. By working together, entomologists and conservationists can hope to secure the fullest representation of the Region's immense and varied woodland fauna.

Lowland heaths and grasslands

Great Orme, Gwynedd. [A.P. Fowles]

Jutting conspicuously out into Conwy Bay is the spectacular, three-kilometre long outcrop of Carboniferous Limestone known as Great Orme's Head. This remarkable site, with its steep cliffs and plateau grasslands, is the best known of the North Wales limestone habitats and has long been noted for its entomological interest. However, unimproved calcareous grasslands are comparatively frequent in a narrow band across the Region, occurring on outcrops in Anglesey and in places on either side of the Vale of Clwyd and southwards down beyond Oswestry. Neutral and acidic grasslands are still to be found locally in both Gwynedd and Clwyd but not to the same extent as the 'rhosydd' etc. of Dyfed and South Wales. Although traditional agriculture predominates over the uplands of North Wales, at lower altitudes there has been widespread drainage and reseeding such that hay meadows and wet pastures are now scarce. On the steeper slopes of the limestone escarpments, however, the soils are often too thin to make ploughing viable and it is these remnants that are so important for the diverse flora and fauna of such habitats.

Limestone outcrops are generally uncommon in Wales and, whilst both of the other Regions have their examples, it is in North Wales that the greatest extent is to be found.

It is readily appreciated that the flora of the limestone grasslands differs markedly from non-calcareous sites and this is also reflected in the invertebrates. The presence or absence of particular foodplants is a major cause but the chemical nature of the soil also plays a significant role in determining which species can survive. On southerly facing slopes, drought can be another critical factor as rainfall seeps easily into cracks and fissures in the limestone beyond the reach of most surface-active species. In the summer months, invertebrates must be able to cope with high ground temperatures during the day and long periods when the soil may be baked dry. In fact, for much of midsummer it can be hard work finding ground-active species as they tend to retreat into the more humid recesses of screes or into the deeper soils which may retain some moisture. Spring and autumn are far more suitable for surveys of beetles and spiders, for

26

instance. This is not to suggest that a summer visit is entirely unproductive as bees and wasps will be busily provisioning their nursery cells and many plant-feeding insects will be in the adult stage, the butterflies being the most conspicuous.

To most entomologists, Great Orme's fame resides in its two endemic subspecies of butterflies — the silver-studded blue *Plebejus argus caernensis* and the grayling *Hipparchia semele thyone*. Both butterflies are considerably smaller than the typical subspecies and emerge earlier in the season. They are both common on Great Orme and the silver-studded blue was also introduced to the Dulas Valley, fifteen kilometres further east, about fifty years ago and is now well-established. The moths of the Creuddyn peninsula (of which Great Orme is the tip) include several national rarities which breed on the limestone plants. Small colonies of the cistus forester *Adscita geryon*, here far removed from their nearest neighbouring populations in Cumbria and the Peak District, occur where there is common rock-rose. Rock-rose is also the foodplant for another of Great Orme's specialities, the silky wave *Idaea dilutaria*, which is otherwise only known from the Bristol area. Of particular interest amongst the micro-Lepidoptera are *Coleophora serpylletorum*, only recently discovered here breeding on thyme and otherwise only known in Britain from Cornwall, and the rare plume moth *Pterophorus spilodactylus*, which feeds on white horehound. Whether or not this extraordinary richness of rare species occurs amongst other invertebrate groups on Great Orme is not clear. The pollen beetle *Meligethes brevis* occurs here on hoary rock-rose and is apparently elsewhere restricted to fragments of limestone grassland near Scarborough. Other beetle records from Great Orme include several scarce species, such as *Aphthona herbigrada*, *Apion urticarium*, *Trachyphloeus alternans* and *Limobius borealis*, which reflect the richness of the limestone flora. The tiny ant *Leptothorax tuberum* and the harvestman *Odiellus spinosus* are other uncommon, southern species found here, but the recording effort for such groups on Great Orme cannot match that for the Lepidoptera. At present this nationally important site is grazed by sheep and feral goats, which are essential to prevent gorse and scrub invasion on the plateau grasslands. On the cliff slopes, exposure combines with goat grazing to hold the thickets in check but it is a fine balance to maintain between over-grazing and scrub encroachment. Nonetheless, nature conservation is at the forefront of management on this Country Park and the outstanding fauna should survive indefinitely. In the meantime, more information from

invertebrate zoologists on the beetles, spiders, bugs, flies, snails, etc. of the Orme will help protect that richness from developments in years to come.

In a few sheltered areas inland of the Orme, the grassland fauna of the limestone is enhanced by scattered scrub which, if not too dense, can add considerably to the invertebrate diversity of a site. On the small limestone pavement of Bryn Pydew nature reserve the moths include the square-spot dart *Euxoa obelisca*, light feathered rustic *Agrotis cinerea* and pretty chalk carpet *Melanthia procellata*, as well as the juniper pug *Eupithecia pusillata* and juniper carpet *Thera juniperata*. The leaf beetle *Chrysolina oricalcia*, which feeds on umbellifers, is the most noteworthy species recorded amongst the other invertebrate orders but much of interest must remain to be discovered. From the available information it appears that a comparable fauna occurs on the steep slopes of the Dulas valley between Colwyn Bay and Abergele. At this point the limestone turns inland and runs southeast down the flanks of the Vale of Clwyd. The limestone here in Denbighshire and across the Afon Clwyd in Flintshire is far less well-known entomologically, but towards the southern end of this range, on the slopes of Bryn Alun, the local pill woodlouse *Armadillidium pulchellum* is known from the limestone screes, and this is one of very few Welsh sites for the leaf beetle *Chrysolina violacea*. Further south-east, the imposing scarp of Eglwyseg Mountain rears up above Llangollen, perhaps too heavily sheep-grazed to be of prime interest for invertebrates but certainly worthy of more investigation than it has received so far.

Limestone also underlies much of eastern Anglesey but glacial drift masks most of the country rock and the few remaining fragments of unimproved calcareous grassland appear to be too small to be of particular significance for invertebrate conservation. The chief interest at sites such as Cors Goch and Graig Wen is that the limestone abuts rich fens and wet heaths. Indeed, the lowland heaths of Anglesey, with the exception of part of Cors Geirch NNR on the Lleyn Peninsula, are the best examples of this habitat type in the Region. This juxtaposition of limestone and wet heath is an ideal combination for base-rich springs and flushes, a feature which can potentially support an important fauna, chiefly of flies with aquatic and semi-aquatic larvae. Unfortunately, recent studies carried out by the Welsh Peatland Invertebrate Survey of the Nature Conservancy Council failed to detect any species of particular conservation importance on these eastern Anglesey heaths but future surveys may be more productive.

It is most often the seepages, ponds or small mires within wet heath that are of the greatest significance for invertebrate conservation as the fauna of the heathland proper is generally widespread on the more abundant moorlands or in managed and degraded peatlands at lower altitudes. However, on Holy Island an extensive wet heath dissected with rocky outcrops has one of the few Welsh populations of the bog bush cricket *Metrioptera brachyptera*, sharing its haunts with a spectacular colony of marsh gentians. Mossy habitats here have yielded the scarce pselaphid beetles *Pselaphaulax dresdensis* and *Bibloplectus spinosus* whilst the uncommon flea beetle *Longitarsus holsaticus* occurs on lousewort. This heath is cattle grazed and occasionally burnt, although the fires probably rarely reach the wetter habitats of greatest importance. Studies on the small heaths of Cors Erddreiniog NNR have shown that burning can have a detrimental effect upon the invertebrate fauna. An introduced colony of silver-studded blues at Cors Erddreiniog survives, and is perhaps dependent upon, rotational burning, but the Welsh Peatland Invertebrate Survey demonstrated that groups with essentially different life histories, such as the Hemiptera and Carabidae, suffer major reductions in the diversity and abundance of species. Burning should really be seen as a last resort for management and should only be carried out piecemeal and over a long timescale to allow invertebrates the opportunity to recover and occupy their preferred stage of the heathland succession.

This management prescription applies equally to both wet and dry lowland heaths but creates a dilemma where, as on the RSPB reserve at South Stack on Holy Island, large areas are covered by dense uniform stands of building-phase heath. Exposure to strong winds and salt-spray on the steeper cliff slopes maintains a varied structure to the coastal heath but on the more level ground of the cliff-tops western gorse, bell heather and ling mature unchecked, forming an impenetrable 'thicket' of heath that is of limited significance for invertebrate conservation. South Stack supports the largest colony in Wales of the heathland form of the silver-studded blue, a butterfly which has declined considerably in Britain this century. As with most 'blue' butterflies, its caterpillars have an association with ants and this probably contributes significantly to the silver-studded blue's preference for short heathland vegetation. Both the caterpillars and the ants benefit from the higher ground temperatures experienced in such situations. In mature heathland it is generally only along the edge of footpaths and trackways that suitable conditions occur and it has been estimated, for instance, that less than 2% of the area of heathland at the north end of Holy Island is occupied by silver-studded blues. Burning can rapidly create ideal habitat for breeding but it is a fairly short-term solution as the heath will revegetate to become too dense within about five years. Physical disturbance of the heathland soil, as from trampling by humans or grazing stock, prevents closed heath from developing for about ten years and is therefore a more preferable management option. Ideally, the introduction of light grazing, as mentioned in the Coastlands Chapter, should be seen as the desired form of management, but where this is impracticable then mechanical disturbance may be necessary. Mowing strips of mature heath,

Bog bush cricket *Metrioptera brachyptera*. [J. Porter]

raking off the litter, and scarifying the soil can be a useful alternative to grazing.

By opening up pockets of bare soil in this way a valuable pioneer habitat is formed which will be beneficial to a variety of coastal invertebrates. Throughout Britain, conservation management frequently means maintaining habitats at a middle phase of their succession and the many invertebrate species that are dependent upon early successional stages are increasingly threatened. The fauna of dry heaths is particularly dominated by species which require sparsely-vegetated soils for breeding, basking or hunting. The behaviour of grayling butterflies on coastal heaths provides an obvious demonstration of this. Less conspicuous will be the ground-active predators, such as spiders, ground beetles and assassin bugs, or the numerous species of solitary bee and wasp that burrow into the soil. These aspects of the invertebrate fauna of the North Wales coastal heaths are little-studied but an interesting assemblage of species can be anticipated to occur. Naturally there are some species which will inhabit other phases of the heathland succession. To conserve as complete a range of the fauna as possible, management should aim towards ensuring that heath is present in all its forms, from bare ground to clumps of heather decaying from old age. In these late stages, heather litter can provide an environment for species such as the harvestman *Paroligolophus meadii*, an uncommon scavenger that, outside England and Wales, is only known from Guernsey and northern Spain. Although reasonably widespread in southern Britain, it is a member of the heathland fauna for which we have a particular international responsibility. Also of geographical interest is the presence of the lesser cockroach *Ectobius panzeri* at South Stack, its northernmost British locality. This small native species is also known from Newborough Warren and Valley Lakes but otherwise its nearest colonies are on the Pembrokeshire coast. Another orthopteran, the grey bush cricket *Platycleis albopunctata*, was known from cliffs near Pwllheli on Lleyn at its northernmost site in

Britain but it has not been recorded (perhaps not searched for) since 1973. The coastal heaths are rather neglected by entomologists in North Wales but their extent and quality around Anglesey and Lleyn suggest that they could be profitable areas for survey. The scarce, predominantly western, chafer *Amphimallon ochraceus* is known from South Stack and one or two other sites but much more of interest must remain to be discovered.

Heaths and grasslands are habitats which must receive continual management if they are to sustain their importance for wildlife. Information on the invertebrate communities present is essential if conservation is to be completely successful. Both habitat types were once much more widespread in North Wales and if a catastrophe befell a particular site (e.g. uncontrolled fires, over-grazing or prolonged neglect) there would have been nearby sites to provide reservoirs for eventual recolonisation. As the unimproved habitats of our lowland countryside become more and more fragmented it is inevitable that local extinctions will become permanent and the former richness of these treasured sites will be diminished forever. As an example, on current knowledge it is believed that there are about thirty colonies of marsh fritillaries *Eurodryas aurinia* scattered across Gwynedd (none survive in Clwyd). Many of these are on the *Molinia* grasslands on the fringe of the uplands and a few are on the lowland wet heaths of Lleyn and Anglesey. However, they are all fairly isolated from each other and, as marsh fritillaries are notoriously prone to localised extinctions, the future for this attractive butterfly is far from assured in the Region. Other species sharing its habitat — the jewel beetle *Trachys troglodytes* or the forester moth *Adscita statices*, for instance — may also be threatened if management does not recognise, and account for, the needs of heathland and grassland invertebrates. Habitat monitoring, based on the ecological requirements of the fauna, will become increasingly necessary. It is no longer enough to extol the virtues of traditional agricultural practices; the lowland landscape has changed too much for that.

Open water and its margins

Yr Wyddfa, Gwynedd. [P. Wakely]

Each year, over 2000 millimetres of rainfall descends upon the high ground of Snowdonia and over 5000 mm per annum falls on the summit of Snowdon itself. This deluge fills the glacial corries and seeps into shallow, trickling streams as they begin their headlong journey, growing ever larger, to the sea. The landscape of this mountain wilderness is sprinkled with gleaming lakes and pools or the white-water torrents of the stony rivers and each, even in this bleak environment, has its own freshwater life. Although far removed from the familiar image of the lowland, reed-fringed lake or the sluggish, meandering river, these montane water-bodies are equally important for wildlife and have their own suite of species adapted for life in the hills. The high altitude corrie lakes are cold and nutrient-poor, a seemingly sterile world, but here the tiny pea mussel *Pisidium conventus* has survived since glacial times. The ameliorating climate has left this arctic species stranded in a few montane lakes in the Scottish Highlands, the Lake District and Snowdonia. It often lives at great depths in the middle of lakes and tarns and

must certainly occur in more than its handful of known sites, but it is undoubtedly a restricted and interesting member of the upland fauna. There are also some species of water beetle that are evidently glacial relics in these cold lakes and which occur nowhere else in Wales, notably *Potamonectes griseostriatus* and *Agabus arcticus. Dytiscus lapponicus* is probably also in the same category, as it is otherwise confined to northern and western Scotland, but its only definite Welsh site is the comparatively low-altitude lake of Llyn-y-parc. These species have all been present on Snowdonia for several thousands of years whilst the surrounding landscape has changed from tundra to sheepwalk. Perhaps they will survive there for as long into the future, although now they must contend with the potentially harmful effects of acidification resulting from air pollution or temperature changes from global warming. Even in these undisturbed, remote and ancient habitats, our impact on the environment can make its mark.

Stoneflies and mayflies typify the freshwater

30

fauna of the upland streams and the stony middle reaches as they are most characteristic of clean, well-oxygenated water. Throughout Snowdonia there is a distinct group of species to be found in the higher altitude watercourses, including *Capnia vidua*, *Protonemura montana*, *Amphinemura standfussi* and *Ameletus inopinatus*. They have been recorded from streams on each of the major mountain blocks and are probably widespread in Gwynedd. Acidification may cause population reductions in some areas but it is unlikely that the fauna of the moorland streams is in need of any particular conservation measures. It is when the rivers descend into the lowlands that they meet with the nationwide problems that threaten our freshwater invertebrates.

There are four major rivers in North Wales — the Dyfi, Conwy, Clwyd and Dee. The Dee is the largest and also the most important for conservation, both in biological and geomorphological terms. Paradoxically, it has also suffered the most damage and it serves as an interesting example of the way in which river systems are affected by Man's activities in the environment. For instance, the tributaries of the Upper Dee were known to contain very diverse stonefly faunas (the Hirnant below Bala had at least twenty-one species) but some of these will have been affected by afforestation of the catchment. Studies in South Wales have demonstrated the detrimental effects of afforestation on stream invertebrates as a result of shading and changes in water chemistry and flow-patterns. Studies have not been carried out on the Dee tributaries but it can be expected that similar results would be found. At least there is now a widespread realisation of the problems of catchment afforestation and efforts are being made to lessen the damage by careful forest design.

The Dee is a major source of water for both domestic and industrial use, supplying millions of gallons each year to the conurbations in its lower reaches. To ensure a regulated supply to consumers throughout the year, Llyn Tegid (Bala Lake) was modified in the mid 1950s to act as a holding reservoir. This has reduced the frequency of spates and provides a more constant flow of water in the summer months. Many invertebrates will have been affected to a greater or less extent by this alteration of the river's behaviour and two of the Dee's specialities have responded in contrasting ways. The glutinous snail *Myxas glutinosa* was regarded as common on the shores of Llyn Tegid up until 1953, inhabiting the stony, wave-washed banks of the lake. Regulation has resulted in a considerable reduction of water-levels in Llyn Tegid during the summer months,

exposing much more of the shallow shore than occurred under natural conditions. It is believed that *Myxas* was unable to survive these drastic events and, despite several searches, it has not been seen in the lake since. It is just possible that it may occur in an unexplored part of the lake but a recent, comprehensive survey of one of its former strongholds at the southwestern end was unsuccessful. *Myxas* is now extremely rare in Britain and is protected under the terms of Schedule 5 of the Wildlife and Countryside Act, 1981.

The large stonefly *Isogenus nubecula*, in contrast, may have responded positively to regulation. It was only discovered in the Dee in 1959 so its abundance prior to regulation is unknown. However, regular surveys since then have indicated that it is extending its range and becoming generally more abundant. In Britain it has only been reliably recorded from the Dee but abroad, where it is regarded as rare in most of Europe, it typically inhabits the stony bed of large rivers with consistent flows. It is possible that regulation has enhanced conditions in the Dee for *Isogenus*. Pollution from farm effluents was thought to have affected its population at one stage and must be an ever-present threat. Fortunately, the Dee's water quality is classed as Grade 1 for most of its length and it is only in the lower reaches that industrial pollution becomes an inevitable hazard.

Other aquatic invertebrates of the Dee include the rare caddisfly *Ylodes simulans* and the tiny, attractive water beetle *Bidessus minutissimus*. *Bidessus* has vanished from several of its former sites through pollution and channel modification and it has been lost from the Conwy due to the accumulation of silt in the stretches of fine gravel it used to favour. Changes in the deposition of sediments brought about by river-straightening schemes or water-abstraction can have a devastating effect on the river fauna. The smooth surface of the river hides a multitude of different habitats below, each supporting different species of invertebrates that are dependent upon the river sustaining their preferred conditions year after year. These may be long riffles or deep pools, patches of aquatic vegetation, submerged tree roots, etc. The capacity of a river to transport heavy particles in suspension depends largely upon the speed it travels and hence alterations in water-flow affect the type of sediment that is carried downstream. Regulation invariably slows the flow during times of spate, whilst channel-straightening can speed up the river and at the same time deny the river opportunities to erode material from its banks. In both cases there is a reduction in the potential supply of gravels downstream, leading to the possibility of some river habitats becoming choked with silt or scoured by the racing water. The development of aquatic vegetation will also change and gradually the character of the river will alter and with it its particular communities of invertebrates.

It is not only the aquatic species which depend upon the deposition of river sediments as there are many terrestrial and semi-aquatic invertebrates that inhabit river banks. River shingle is a particularly rich habitat for a number of specialised beetles, flies and spiders of restricted distribution nationally. It is becoming clear that the Welsh gravel-bed rivers are of great interest in this respect, although the extent of the resource in North Wales is as yet poorly known. Historical records are chiefly concerned with the riparian ground beetles and a selection of these records will indicate the potential to be discovered. Rare species include *Thalassophilus longicornis*, known from Maentwrog and Betws-y-coed, *Perileptus areolatus* on the Afon Ceiriog, *Bembidion prasinum* at Llanfairfechan, and *Bembidion geniculatum* reported from the Afon Dwyfor. Unfortunately, the specific localities for these species are not recorded but searches of suitable shingle banks remaining in the vicinity would be worth exploring. Recent investigations of the Afon Mawddach at Llanelltyd have yielded promising results. On the excellent shingle bars here *Perileptus areolatus* occurs with the nationally rare rove beetle *Scopaeus gracilis*, the characteristic shingle aleocharines *Hydrosmecta thinobioides* and *Hydrosmectina subtillissima*, and the scarce spiders *Arctosa cinerea* and *Caviphantes saxetorum*. As long as the rivers are free to deposit and work sediments along their length then these important habitats will continue to exist. There is a need to identify the best stretches, however, as shingle is often seen as an easy source of hardcore and excavation can obviously be very damaging. There is also evidence that stock-trampling results in an impoverished fauna as the shingle matrix is repeatedly churned up. Whilst some Diptera, for instance, may benefit from this type of poaching, it is a common feature of Welsh rivers and undisturbed examples need to be protected from stock access for the scarcer elements of the fauna.

Riverside habitats, in general, are rather neglected entomologically in North Wales and there is plenty of scope for rewarding and useful survey. Carr woodland is a particularly valuable habitat with a distinctive fauna. Cefn-y-bedd on the banks of the Afon Alun is a good example, containing a rich cranefly assemblage including *Gonomyia abbreviata, Limonia trivittata, Limonia*

inusta and *Molophilus corniger*. The wooded banks of the Dee at Erbistock have considerable potential and calcareous streams joining the river here support the scarce caddisflies *Adicella filicornis, Plectrocnemia brevis* and *Ernodes articularis*. Well-developed river fen is not common in the Region but can be expected to contain a good diversity of invertebrates where it does occur. The tidal reedswamp and associated willow carr at Dolgarrog on the Conwy is a haunt of the impressive musk beetle *Aromia moschata* and the locally distributed weevil *Cryptorhynchus lapathi* is also present. On the banks of the Glaslyn at Pont Croesor the whorl snail *Vertigo lilljeborgi* occurs at one of its few Welsh sites. Throughout the Region, rivers and their peripheral habitats are a major wildlife feature. There is a tradition of aquatic survey which should be maintained and strengthened by riparian surveys in order to promote the requirements of invertebrate conservation in studies of river corridors. Nature conservation is now an accepted part of river management and invertebrates should also be accommodated in future decisions regarding the use and enjoyment of the Region's watercourses.

Most of the natural lakes in North Wales have formed in depressions of glacial origin in the hard rocks of the uplands. These lakes are generally nutrient-poor but the numerous shallow lakes on Anglesey tend to be eutrophic with dense aquatic and emergent vegetation and an entirely different fauna. Interesting species occur from many invertebrate groups but these lakes are chiefly known for their excellent dragonflies, particularly the hairy dragonfly *Brachytron pratense* and the variable damselfly *Coenagrion pulchellum*. Llyn Cerrig Bach, one of the Valley lakes, is noted for its scarce water beetles, including the whirligig *Gyrinus paykulli* in its only known Welsh site and its close relative *G. suffriani*, which is also restricted in Wales to Anglesey. Other standing water habitats of interest on the island include the sandy pools of Newborough Forest which, in addition to scarce dragonflies and beetles, contain a population of medicinal leeches *Hirudo medicinalis*, one of about twenty surviving populations in Britain. There are modern records of the medicinal leech from three sites on Anglesey, two of which are shallow, eutrophic ponds with dense stands of vegetation and the third is the somewhat atypical fen habitat of Cors Goch.

Malltraeth Marsh is now an extensive network of drainage ditches in the Cefni valley in the south-east of the island. Its ditches, and the old oxbows of the canalised Afon Cefni, support a rich flora and surveys have revealed the presence

***Colletes cunicularius* (Hymenoptera):** Nesting aggregations of this rare bee occur in firm sand on dune systems in western Britain. The bees visit creeping willow blossom in spring to collect pollen for their cells.
(Photograph by Prema Photos.)

Horton Cliffs, Gower: Coastal footpaths can be important for burrowing insects, such as bees or oil beetles, as they provide patches of bare soil in sunny situations. Unimproved heaths and grasslands on the cliff-top provide valuable foraging for bees and wasps.
(Photograph by A.P. Fowles.)

Porth Neigwl, Lleyn: Part of the four kilometres long stretch of soft-rock cliffs at the tip of the Lleyn Peninsula. This is probably the best example of this naturally scarce habitat in Wales, although other shorter stretches also occur on Lleyn.
(Photograph by A.P. Fowles.)

Coed Ganllwyd, Gwynedd: Woodland watercourses are amongst our most natural habitats, their environmental conditions having remained little changed for several thousand years. On ancient sites, a rich fauna thrives in the luxuriant streamside mosses and the damp soil and leaf litter along the banks.
(Photograph by P. Wakely.)

Gwern Llywyn-gwyn, Dyfed: Established carr woodland, such as this stand of old alders, is a valuable habitat for invertebrates that breed in wet rotten wood, fungi, or saturated peat and soil.
(Photograph by A.O. Chater.)

***Limax tenellus* (Mollusca):** Ancient woodlands are the haunt of this scarce slug, where it is most frequently found feeding on boletus fungi. It is regarded as a good indicator species of old oak woodlands in Wales.
(Photograph by D.G. Rands.)

Parc Pont-faen, Dyfed: There are relatively few pasture-woodlands in Wales with old oak trees and their conservation is important for a wide range of species associated with dead and dying timber.
(Photograph by A.P. Fowles.)

Medicinal leech *Hirido medicinalis*.
[R.S. Key]

of seventy-four species of water beetle. Some of these, such as *Noterus crassicornis*, *Ilybius guttiger* and *Rhantus grapii*, are uncommon fenland species but the ditches do not seem to contain the rarer fenland relicts, such as *Graptodytes granularis*, which are known elsewhere on the island. Malltraeth is second only to the Gwent Levels as an example of grazing marsh habitat in Wales, although it lacks the diversity of substrate and water chemistry of the larger site. It is not likely to be as entomologically-rich as the Gwent Levels but should, nonetheless, prove to be an important site when fully surveyed. There

appears to be little information on the Diptera of Malltraeth and this must surely be a profitable aspect to explore in the future.

With the scarcity of ditch systems of conservation value in Wales it is important that the best examples are managed for the benefit of both their flora and fauna. It can be easy to overlook the abundant animal life that lives and breeds beneath the surface of our freshwater habitats or along their margins, yet their conservation depends on our vigilance and effort as much as any of the species of the terrestrial habitats do.

Lowland peatlands

Fenn's Moss, Clwyd. [A.P. Fowles]

Before Man began to clear the forests for primitive agriculture, lowland Britain was almost entirely covered by woodland. A narrow fringe of coastal habitats would have been present, maintained as they are today by the natural processes of wind and tide, but inland there would have been few open areas free of trees except on lake margins or the floodplains of rivers. Since the end of the last period of glaciation these waterlogged pockets of land have steadily developed into peatlands and by the time grasslands and heathlands began to appear there would have already been an extensive area of lowland peat in Britain. Radiocarbon dating shows that many of our peatlands began to form between six and eight thousand years ago and hence they are amongst our most ancient habitats. Peatland faunas have therefore had a considerable time to establish, with some species presumably moving down from the tundra above the tree-line and others colonising from the continent. Bogs and fens would have been widely-distributed across Britain, facilitating the expansion of range of newly-arrived

invertebrates, and populations of most species must have been more widespread and comparatively abundant. Distribution was largely governed by climate and water chemistry until recent times when peat-cutting and subsequent attempts at drainage began to disrupt peatland ecology. Of course, in these early stages, from the Middle Ages onwards, interference would have been negligible in terms of the extent of peatland available. It would not have been until the beginning of the nineteenth century that significant damage occurred as landowners began to realise that major, labour-intensive, drainage schemes could reclaim the intractable bog-lands for agriculture. It is, therefore, only in the past two hundred years or so that lowland peatlands have been under any serious threat, but in that time a massive reduction and deterioration of the habitat has occurred throughout lowland Britain. Damage accelerated dramatically in the middle of this century and the impetus of grant-aid and technological innovations in the 1970s brought about a threat to the existence of lowland peatlands altogether. Recognising this, the Nature

Conservancy Council established the Welsh Lowland Peatland Survey in 1976 to attempt to identify, on botanical grounds, remaining sites of high conservation value. In the same year, a small group of entomological specialists surveyed the best fens in North Wales for a week —the first major invertebrate survey to be carried out in Wales. Both of these studies reinforced the belief that North Wales contained a number of exceptional peatland sites and the calcareous valley fens of Anglesey and Lleyn, in particular, were singled out for their considerable importance for invertebrate conservation.

Peatland conservation continues to be a major focus of activity in Wales and recently the Welsh Peatland Invertebrate Survey has carried out a major investigation of the fauna of most of the best sites in the Principality. This included extensive sampling on twenty-six lowland peatlands in North Wales and the information generated has led to a fuller understanding of the invertebrate communities present in different peatland habitats and indicated some of the responses of the fauna to different management strategies.

In simple terms, peatlands consist of a range of plant communities growing on a waterlogged substrate. Plant-feeding invertebrates will obviously require the correct foodplant to be present, perhaps under specific conditions, before they can breed successfully. Other species that breed in moss, leaf-litter, bare peat or water will be governed chiefly by the physical structure of the habitat or the prevailing water chemistry. In all cases, management or its absence will be a critical factor for the survival of different species and now that the vast majority of the better peatlands in North Wales are protected as Sites of Special Scientific Interest the question of management is the most pressing concern. The first priority is to ensure that a high water-table is maintained and that groundwater input is unpolluted and guaranteed. Fortunately, there are few problems in Wales with water-abstraction depriving peatlands of groundwater but this is a possible threat to limestone springs feeding the Anglesey calcareous fens. Once the correct water-table is established, subsequent management will depend largely upon the type of peatland, the plant communities present, and the land-use history. Raised (ombrotrophic) mires, unless damaged in the past, should not require any management and should certainly not be burnt or grazed as this will undoubtedly be to the detriment of the habitat structure and its invertebrates. Fens (minerotrophic mires), on the other hand, are very diverse and there is an equally varied assortment of invertebrate

communities associated with the different conditions created by management. There are invertebrate species of conservation importance to be found in the full range of habitat types occurring across the spectrum of management, as long as those activities are consistent with maintaining the health of the peatland habitat in general. The sensible approach is to continue with traditional practices, though with the caveat that intensive grazing or frequent burning will have already impoverished the fauna.

Undamaged raised mires have grown beyond the influence of groundwater and are dependent upon rainfall and other forms of precipitation. They receive very little nutrient input and hence are dominated by acidophilous vegetation, mainly *Sphagnum* mosses and heather. Higher plant diversity is poor and the invertebrate fauna is characteristically composed of a limited range of species. This raised mire community contains few rarities but is of ecological significance as it represents a natural assemblage that has been little modified by Man. Lowland raised mires are not well-represented in North Wales and the three significant examples have all been historically damaged to some extent. Arthog Bog in Merioneth, whilst retaining some of its botanical interest, no longer supports a raised mire fauna as drainage has substantially lowered the water-table. The vegetation is now poor-fen and the invertebrates, too, are typical of this widespread habitat type. Nonetheless, Arthog Bog is a large peatland and of some value for invertebrate conservation, although it has lost its original distinctive community. Drainage on the mid-altitude mire of Cors Goch Trawsfynydd has been less severe and an ombrotrophic dome still survives intact. The ground beetle *Agonum ericeti*, which is restricted to raised mires, is present and the large heath butterfly *Coenonympha tullia* occurs at one of its relatively few Welsh sites. The extensive margins of this raised dome have been affected by peat-cutting, grazing and inefficient drainage but the water-table is still high and the resulting peatland habitats support a rich assemblage of invertebrates characteristic of acidic mires.

In the east of the Region, the enormous complex of Fenn's, Whixall and Bettisfield Mosses (consisting of some 680 ha) is one of the most famous entomological localities in Wales. Over the past century this site has yielded an extraordinary number of invertebrate rarities and it is an important example of the once widespread mosses of the Cheshire-Shropshire plain, few of which survive today. The complex straddles the Clwyd/Shropshire border and it is not always clear from past records to which country they pertain. However, most of the moss is in Wales, including most of the undamaged mire surface, and it can be assumed that many of the rarer species occur in Wales. Fenn's Moss has experienced substantial damage, both historically and in recent times, and it is quite remarkable that it manages to sustain such an outstanding wildlife interest. This is the result of two main factors: the size of the moss has allowed species to continue breeding in sections remote from contemporary disturbance; and the damage from traditional peat-cutting occurred at a pace which enabled invertebrates to recolonise in time from nearby habitat. Unfortunately, the hydrology of the mire has been severely disrupted, both by the construction of the Shropshire Union Canal (which isolates the now wooded Bettisfield Moss) and a network of peripheral drains. In recent years, the accelerated rate of commercial peat extraction has exacerbated the situation and the majority of the central core is covered by bracken, birch and *Molinia*. Now that Fenn's Moss has been purchased as a National Nature Reserve the long, slow process of restoring the water-table and rejuvenating the mire surface must begin. It is neither likely nor desirable that the whole area will return to ombrotrophic mire and management will be designed to cater for the substantial range of species which have become established on the traditional peat-cuttings.

When the moss was intact, white-faced dragonflies *Leucorrhinia dubia* probably bred in the bog pools of the hummock-hollow zone on the centre of the dome. As these pools vanished through peat-cutting and the general drying-out of the moss, they would have found the *Sphagnum* hollows of old peat-cuttings an acceptable alternative and this is the habitat they occupy today. These old peat-cuttings became an integral part of the ecology of the moss and other scarce species, such as *Agonum ericeti* and the shore bug *Micracanthia marginalis*, have probably depended upon them during the most recent phase of extraction. The invading birch scrub has an interesting fauna, too, including the large red-belted clearwing *Synanthedon culiciformis* and the weevil *Curculio betulae*. On the edge of Bettisfield Moss, the nationally rare peatland caddisfly *Hagenella clathrata* inhabits wet areas between grass tussocks, one of only four known populations in Britain.

Although Fenn's and Whixall Mosses have been famous collecting grounds for entomologists for a very long time it is clear that a great deal remains to be learnt about their invertebrate fauna. The Lepidoptera are probably the best-studied group and 'Whixall Moss' (as the area has been traditionally known) is revered for its populations of the Manchester treble bar *Carsia sororiata*, northern footman *Eilema sericea*, and the *davus* form of the large heath. The micro-Lepidoptera, however, have received much less attention. Orthoptera, with both lesser marsh grasshopper *Chorthippus albomarginatus* and bog bush cricket *Metrioptera brachyptera* present, and Odonata have probably been fully documented and there is a reasonable amount of information on the spider fauna, which includes *Singa hamata* and *Dolomedes fimbriatus*. The water beetles have been surveyed but there is little information on other Coleoptera families and groups such as the Hemiptera and Hymenoptera are almost completely unknown. There are a number of important Diptera records from the middle of the century but modern surveys would be very useful. In 1936 a specimen of the cranefly *Limnophila heterogyna* was taken on 'Whixall Moss', the only record of the species in Britain, and the horse fly *Atylotus plebeius* was found in 1955. This latter species used to be a speciality of the mosses of the Cheshire-Shropshire plain but there have been no British records since 1956. With the opportunity for conservation management on Fenn's Moss at last in hand this is certainly an apposite time to comprehensively document the invertebrate fauna. The devastating wounds of recent years will eventually heal but, in the meantime, invertebrate surveys will be of great benefit in ensuring that the full richness of this outstanding site survives the change from peat extraction to peatland conservation.

Apart from Fenn's Moss, Clwyd is not favoured with many lowland peatlands of conservation interest. Those that are left are essentially of two types, small acidic basins and mesotrophic valley fens. The basins, such as Vicarage Moss near Gresford, have a limited fauna consisting of typical species that are generally widespread in Wales. The valley fens, notably Gatewen Marsh, Sontley Moor and Merddwr, are more diverse in terms of habitats and their associated faunas but records so far indicate, once again, that they are merely good local examples of a fairly common invertebrate assemblage. Of course, these species can only be regarded as 'fairly common' whilst such sites continue to provide habitats for them and should not be dismissed because they are, fortunately, not rare. The existence of a typical fen invertebrate community over a wide area of Wales is a strong-point and indicates the overall health of the peatland resource. Sontley Moor differs from the other Clwyd fens in the presence of calcareous, tufa-depositing, springs which have a localised influence upon the peat. The caddisfly *Ernodes articulatus*, a rare British species, develops

Raft spider *Dolomedes fimbriatus*.
[S.G. Ball]

in these trickles along with larvae of the scirtid beetle *Cyphon pubescens*.

Calcareous springs and seepages are more characteristic of the renowned rich fens of Anglesey and the Lleyn Peninsula, a suite of peatlands unique in Wales and with few comparable examples elsewhere in Britain. The Anglesey fens have developed on pro-glacial lakes which occupied valley basins between ridges of Carboniferous Limestone and hence are of alkaline peat influenced by the calcareous groundwater. Marl, the calcified remains of stoneworts, was dug from some of them to be used as an agricultural fertiliser and small-scale peat-cutting for fuel was widely practised. Three fen plants (great fen-sedge, black bog rush and blunt-flowered rush) are highly characteristic, although botanically the fens are extremely diverse and the varied flora contributes significantly to their importance for phytophagous invertebrates. The National Nature Reserve of Cors Geirch is the best example of this type of peatland on Lleyn (where there are few other rich fens) but Anglesey has several excellent sites in the limestone country of the Malltraeth Trough in the eastern half of the island. Cors Erddreiniog NNR is probably the best known but other important sites include Cors Goch, a North Wales Wildlife Trust reserve, and Cors Bodeilio, part of which is an NNR.

Cors Geirch occupies a long shallow valley in which calcareous till was deposited by Irish Sea Ice during the last glaciation. As with the Anglesey rich fens, alkaline peat has become established on the site of a former lake and the present-day vegetation is a mixture of *Cladium* fen, reedswamp, willow carr, wet heath, etc. Only part of the site is managed as a National Nature

Reserve and the differing degree of management carried out by the various owners accounts for much of this variation in the plant communities. A high proportion of Cors Geirch is rank, unmanaged fen with *Molinia*, *Juncus* and bog myrtle dominant. This contains a fairly typical 'tall fen' fauna, including species such as the locally distributed soldier beetle *Cantharis thoracica* and the less common leaf hoppers *Megamelodes lequesnei*, *Paradelphacodes paludosus* and *Delphacodes capnodes*. There is undoubtedly some value in retaining an area of unmanaged fen on Cors Geirch but the dangers of succession to scrub woodland are very real. Carr can be an important constituent of fen as it supports its own distinctive fauna and provides shelter for open fen species when required. However, a balance must be maintained which recognises the prime importance of the rich fen itself. Light grazing may be enough to control scrub encroachment if water levels are kept reasonably high.

The rest of the fen is grazed by cattle and/or ponies and the structural mosaic they create by selective grazing and trampling provides ideal conditions for many of the scarcer elements of the rich fen fauna. This is particularly important where there are shallow calcareous seepages as moderate stock densities will produce poached margins for oviposition and prevent shading by rushes and sedges detrimentally affecting the micro-climate of the seepage. Invertebrates recorded from Cors Geirch which are almost certainly linked to these flushes and seepages include the small red damselfly *Ceriagrion tenellum* and the scarce blue-tailed damselfly *Ischnura pumilio*, the scirtid beetle *Cyphon pubescens*, the ground beetle *Elaphrus uliginosus* and the soldier fly *Oxycera pygmaea*. Light grazing also has the effect of forming tussocks in open grassland and, where there is abundant devil's-bit scabious, this is the preferred habitat of the marsh fritillary *Eurodryas aurinia*. The habitat requirements of Cors Geirch's rarest invertebrate species is as yet unknown. A single example of the ground beetle *Chlaenius tristis* was found in a *Sphagnum* tussock in 1976 but subsequent searches have failed to reveal more specimens. There are old records from the East Anglian fens but it had long been considered extinct in Britain before this record. *C. tristis* is also rare and declining in many European countries, where it is most usually associated with lush fens at the edge of lakes. Perhaps Cors Geirch is no longer suitable to maintain a population but if *tristis* is refound it should become the focus of positive management.

Not surprisingly, the fauna of the Anglesey rich fens bears many similarities to Cors Geirch and the management guidelines mentioned above are equally applicable. Regularly occurring species on these North Wales fens include the Hemiptera *Lamproplax picea*, *Pachybrachius fracticollis*, *Paradelphacodes paludosus* and *Delphacodes capnodes*. The hopper *Cicadella lasiocarpae* is more restricted, being presently known only from Cors Erddreiniog, Cors Bodeilio and Cors Geirch in Britain. As its name suggests, it probably feeds on the sedge *Carex lasiocarpa*, but other sedges in the calcareous fens may also serve as its foodplant. The richness of the leaf hopper fauna is reflected in a notable abundance of the parasitic dryinid wasps and one species found on Cors Erddreiniog, *Prenanteon frontalis*, is otherwise only known in Britain from the New Forest. Characteristic Lepidoptera of the fens are the pinion-streaked snout *Schrankia costaestrigalis*, the valerian pug *Eupithecia valerianata* and the silver hook *Eustrotia uncula*, whilst the ground beetles *Blethisa multipunctata* and *Chlaenius nigricornis* are indicative of fens with a high water table.

Whilst the main body of these fens supports a distinctive and valuable fauna, many of the rarest species occur on calcareous seepages at the margins where flushes and springs from the limestone catchment promote tussocky stands of black bog rush and tufa is deposited on cushions of moss. These areas are of great botanical interest and they are also the haunt of several very rare invertebrates. The marvellous seepages at Cors Erddreiniog are a prime example and here the Red Data Book soldier fly *Stratiomys chamaeleon*, a large and conspicuous black and yellow fly, breeds amongst the water-logged sediments. Other noteworthy inhabitants include the beetle *Eubria palustris*, the cranefly *Orimarga*

juvenilis and the whorl snail *Vertigo lilljeborgi*. The occurrence of this latter species on calcareous seepages is most unusual as elsewhere in Britain it is closely associated with acidic or mesotrophic basin and floodplain fens where there is a marked degree of seasonal flooding. The same general area is of further ecological interest for the presence of a small population of the southern damselfly *Coenagrion mercuriale* at its northernmost British site. Here the colony is based on a small calcareous stream which is largely choked with emergent vegetation. The southern damselfly, in the rest of its British range, occupies open, mesotrophic flushes in grazed heathlands and it seems that ponies and sheep at Cors Erddreiniog keep small patches of the stream in sufficiently open conditions to sustain the colony.

Within the scope of this review there is insufficient space to do full justice to the significance of these rich fens to invertebrate conservation but hopefully an impression of their overall importance has been portrayed. There are also many other high quality fen types present in the Region which deserve at least a brief mention. Mesotrophic mires are relatively common in parts of Gwynedd and are represented by a number of fine sites such as Llyn Hafodol on Anglesey, Llyn Ystumllyn on Lleyn, and Cors-y-sarnau in Merioneth. The latter is of chief interest as a geographically-isolated peatland containing a representative fauna whilst the other two, in addition to a wide range of characteristic and uncommon species, are distinguished by the presence of the cranefly *Limonia magnicauda* in its only known Welsh stations. Pont Croesor on the banks of the Afon Glaslyn is an excellent floodplain fen with riverbank carr, a valuable habitat for wetland Diptera and a more typical location for the snail *Vertigo lilljeborgi*. Lowland acidic mires are rather scarce outside Anglesey, where the basin fens of Cors Clegyrog and Salbri are amongst the best examples. In Caernarvonshire, the mid-altitude basin of Cors Graianog and the nearby peatland complex of Cors Gyfelog are exceptional, the latter containing a strong population of the nationally rare weevil *Bagous frit*. Hafod Garregog, an acidic valley mire upstream from Pont Croesor, is a beautiful mixture of wooded knolls, pools, *Molinia* mires and bog myrtle thickets. Despite its unpromising appearance, rank *Molinia* is of some interest and typical species occurring at Hafod Garregog include the lacewing *Psectra diptera* and the money spider *Glyphesis servulus*. This important habitat mosaic is now managed as a National Nature Reserve and when it has received the level of invertebrate survey it deserves it will surely yield a number of significant discoveries.

As outlined earlier, systematic surveys of peatlands in North Wales are a recent phenomenon and we are only now beginning to gain an understanding of what constitutes the typical fauna and what management, if any, is required to maintain its richness. Although the Nature Conservancy Council's Welsh Peatland Invertebrate Survey investigated a large number of the better sites it must be remembered that their samples were selective in terms of method and season. There is a great deal still to be learnt about the fauna of the Region's peatlands and surveys should continue and be encouraged. Peatlands are an ancient, natural heritage and the contribution North Wales makes to the conservation of the habitat type and its invertebrates in Britain is substantial. As with ancient woodlands and mountain peaks, we must ensure that the Welsh countryside continues to provide a home for those species that have lived here for thousands of years undisturbed.

Uplands

Cwm Caseg, Gwynedd. [Nature Conservancy Council]

Yr Wyddfa, the majestic mountain of Snowdon, is the highest peak in England and Wales at 1085 metres above sea level. It is the focal point of Eryri (Snowdonia) and a magnificent feature of the breathtaking landscape of North Wales. Yet it is just one of fourteen peaks above 915 metres (3000 feet) in the Region and there are at least five times as many summits over 760 metres (2000 feet). These familiar statistics encapsulate the reason behind the importance of North Wales for upland invertebrates. Although the rest of the Principality boasts some 60% of its land surface above 300 metres, neither of the other two Regions has anything like the extent of land at higher altitudes that occurs in North Wales. Pumlumon and the Brecon Beacons contain a small number of montane invertebrates but the North Wales mountains mark the southern limit of distribution for many species in Britain. It is believed that these invertebrates have survived as relict populations on the mountain tops, a legacy of Britain's postglacial fauna that has become confined to the bleakest upland habitats as the climate ameliorated following the Ice Age. In fact,

little is known about the population dynamics, environmental factors and competitive pressures which maintain and restrict these species to their mountain haunts but, whatever the reasons, they are a very special part of the Region's fauna. With a lack of ecological data, positive conservation measures are inevitably limited but ensuring their continued existence in North Wales should be a matter of concern, bringing together invertebrate zoologists and the practitioners of nature conservation in an effort to improve our knowledge of upland invertebrates and their requirements.

The most celebrated inhabitant of the North Wales mountains typifies these problems. There can be few more splendid symbols for invertebrate conservation than the beautifully-patterned, and aptly-named, rainbow leaf beetle *Chrysolina cerealis*. In Europe, this is a reasonably widespread species but it is entirely confined in Britain to a few small areas on the flanks of Yr Wyddfa and the neighbouring Glyders. Its existence on these mountains has long been known and there are numerous examples in the

40

entomological literature of Victorian coleopterists showing specimens at exhibitions. On occasions it has been reported as occurring in abundance but there are also several notes in the literature stating that none could be found despite prolonged searches. Most modern records only relate to very small numbers being seen in their favoured localities. It is possible that this elusive insect usually secretes itself by day amongst plant roots and perhaps only has a mass diurnal emergence at a particular point in its life-cycle. However, on the basis of current records the rainbow leaf beetle has been legally protected under Schedule 5 of the Wildlife and Countryside Act, 1981. Although there is no direct evidence that collecting has caused a decline in the population, it is clear that this beautiful beetle has historically been a quarry for 'trophy-hunters'. It is sensible to curtail this practice as detailed studies are needed to reveal the strength of the population and identify possible threats.

Why the rainbow leaf beetle should have such a restricted distribution is a complete mystery as it feeds on wild thyme, which is a widespread plant even in the Welsh uplands. On the acidic rocks of Snowdon and the Glyders, thyme grows within a grassy sward on areas of base-enriched seepage. The foodplant here is small and relatively inconspicuous, not at all like the thick clumps of thyme growing in coastal habitats, and possibly the increased density of sheep on the mountains has affected the capacity of the grassland to sustain large populations of the beetle. Despite the long tradition of collecting, there have been few attempts to understand the ecology of the rainbow leaf beetle. Initial studies have revealed how difficult this species is to monitor and a clearer picture of adult and larval behaviour is required before a valid assessment of its conservation status can be made.

There are two other species of insect which are only found in the upland districts of North Wales and hence of particular conservation concern in the Region. Ashworth's rustic *Xestia ashworthii* is a blue-grey noctuid moth that occurs widely in Snowdonia and on the limestone uplands of Clwyd, and also just extends into Dyfed on the northern fringe of Pumlumon. The larvae are polyphagous on a wide range of low-growing herbs and are associated chiefly with steep cliffs or scree. On the dry ground it favours it is probably confined to such habitats by sheep-grazing, although shelter provided by loose rocks may be important for both adults and larvae. Welsh specimens are classified as a subspecies distinct from populations occurring in the Alps and Scandinavia so there is an extra significance to its conservation here. The other speciality of

the Region is Weaver's wave *Idaea contiguaria*, a geometrid moth which is represented in Wales by the subspecies *brittanica*. Its caterpillars feed upon heather, crowberry and navelwort and it is reasonably widespread in upland Gwynedd but is found nowhere else in Britain. This rather inconspicuous moth appears to have attracted far less attention than the other two North Wales rarities and its habitat requirements are ill-defined. Nonetheless, it is of equal importance in terms of conservation and a comprehensive study of its distribution would be very valuable.

Two other invertebrates have been reported in Britain as occurring only in the mountains of North Wales, the spiders *Micaria alpina* and *Typhochrestus simoni*. Certainly both are of extremely restricted occurrence but the former has now been found in Scotland whilst the latter is known from chalk grassland in southern England. *Micaria* is an arctic-alpine species which hunts for its prey on stony ground at high altitudes. *Typhochrestus* is a montane species in the Alps and its presence on lowland chalk in England is anomalous. The fact that *Micaria* was thought to be confined to North Wales for so long highlights one of the difficulties of invertebrate surveys for montane faunas. Quite simply, fieldwork is arduous, the results often unpredictable, and there is a vast area to be covered. New discoveries will continue to be made and it is even feasible, for instance, that the rainbow leaf beetle exists unknown in localised areas on other summits. This begs the question of whether or not conservation is necessary for upland invertebrates when we cannot be certain of the status of any individual species. The answer has to be affirmative as we cannot gamble with the fate of species because of a lack of knowledge. Invertebrates, be they lowland or upland species, generally occupy small-scale niches in the environment and it is quite possible that the vastness of the British uplands masks our understanding of the precise ecological requirements of the montane fauna. There is no reason to suppose that no invertebrates are confined to specialised microhabitats in the uplands and it is safer for conservationists to assume the opposite until knowledge improves. Afforestation, substantial increases in sheep density, footpath erosion, quarrying and mining have all affected habitat quality over a wide area of the North Wales mountains. Their effect upon upland invertebrates is entirely unknown but some species must undoubtedly have declined in abundance and perhaps others, unnoticed, have become extinct. Detailed information on the invertebrate communities of different habitats on the summits is not available so we must fall back on the procedure of limiting habitat change as far as possible and safeguarding those features of the habitat which are identifiably scarce.

On the open sheepwalks, the richest faunas are associated with tussocky or stony ground that affords some protection from the weather. The limited range of plant species restricts the phytophagous element of the fauna and most of these species are ubiquitous on widespread ericaceous shrubs, sedges and grasses, or sparse herbs. Typical moths include the antler *Cerapteryx graminis*, the northern spinach *Eulithis populata* and the pyralid *Agriphila straminella*. Few plant-feeding beetles occur on high ground but *Micrelus ericae* and *Lochmaea suturalis* are locally abundant on heather and the click beetle *Ctenicera cuprea* is common. Some of the scarcer Lepidoptera are largely restricted to crags where grazing pressure is low, noteworthy species including the red carpet *Xanthorhoe munitata*, the yellow-ringed carpet *Entephria flavicinctata* and perhaps also the scarce and little-known grass moth *Catoptria furcatellus*. The uncommon weevils *Otiorhynchus nodosus* and *Barynotus squamosus* have been recorded from a few of the mountain blocks in North Wales.

Many of the true montane invertebrates of North Wales are predators and generalist scavengers, chiefly carabid and staphylinid beetles and spiders. Much of our knowledge of this aspect of the fauna comes from a series of pitfall trap studies carried out in the late 1960s on most of the higher peaks. In addition to the two species mentioned earlier, the notable upland spiders are represented by *Theridion bellicosum*, *Pardosa trailli*, *Lepthyphantes pinicola*, *L. whymperi*, *Tiso aestivus*, *Entelecara errata* and *Meioneta nigripes*. Not surprisingly, these species are either ground-active hunters or else build their webs on the ground or under stones. Rocky summits, such as the Rhinogau, are ideal habitats, whilst broken carpets of woolly hair moss can also provide suitable cover for some species. Constant trampling by ramblers can seriously disrupt these high-ground environments and it is evident that the better faunas are found on some of the less-visited peaks. Amongst the carabid beetles, *Nebria nivalis* (recorded from Yr Wyddfa) and *Leistus montanus* (Yr Wyddfa, Cadair Idris and Carnedd y Ddelw) are the most interesting inhabitants. Both species are known from just a handful of mountain tops in northern England and Scotland and are not known outside Snowdonia in Wales. More widely distributed carabids in the British uplands include *Nebria gyllenhali*, *Pterostichus adstrictus* and *P. aethiops*. On the Clwydian Range *Miscodera arctica* and *Cymindis vaporariorum* have been recorded in the past, but this interesting

upland block has been comparatively neglected by entomologists in recent years. Less attention has been paid to the rove beetles at high altitude in North Wales but several scarce species have been recorded, chiefly from moss or under stones. *Ocyusa hibernica* (from Cwm Idwal and Yr Wyddfa) is a national rarity known from very few mountains and other notable species include *Geodromicus longipes*, *Anthophagus alpinus* and *Oxypoda tirolensis*.

Mountain summits are a natural focus for investigation but, of course, montane invertebrates are not only restricted to the highest few metres. Habitat structure and the degree of exposure are probably the critical features and relict montane species can occur in suitable conditions anywhere above 600-700 metres in North Wales. Nor is it only the open, dry ground that is of interest as flushes and blanket mires also support a valuable fauna. The scarce cranefly *Dactylolabis sexmaculata* is known from Yr Wyddfa (it is more typically an inhabitant of limestone uplands), where it is possibly associated with base-enriched seepages on the doleritic rocks. Lightly-grazed heather moors and blanket mires are infrequent in the Region but are of great interest for invertebrates. The Rhinogau have some fine areas of tall heather moorland with the characteristic ground beetle *Carabus glabratus* and the localised micro-moths *Fomoria weaveri*, *Phyllonorycter junoniella*, *Olethreutes mygindiana* and *Rhopobota ustomaculana*, all of which feed on cowberry.

The best blanket mire occurs on the extensive uplands of Migneint and Berwyn where vast tracts of peat clothe the shallow slopes. In a few places there are colonies of large heath butterflies *Coenonympha tullia* but they have a very restricted distribution, which is something of a mystery as their foodplant, hare's-tail cottongrass, is abundant in such habitats. Climatic factors and heather-burning are probably responsible for confining the large heath to certain favoured areas. Apart from the small heath *C. pamphilus* and occasional green hairstreaks *Callophrys rubi* (the latter on bilberry moors), the only frequent resident butterfly of the blanket mires is the small pearl-bordered fritillary *Boloria selene* which is not uncommon, particularly on the lower, sheltered slopes. Several moths are very characteristic of blanket mires, such as the common heath *Ematurga atomaria* and the true lover's knot *Lycophotia porphyrea*, whilst grey mountain carpets *Entephria caesiata* and wood tigers *Parasemia plantaginis* are frequently encountered. Scarcer residents include the grey scalloped bar *Dyscia fagaria*, the golden-rod brindle *Lithomoia solidaginis*, Haworth's minor *Celaena haworthi* and

Wood tiger *Parasemia plantaginis*. [J. Porter]

the scarce silver Y *Autographa interrogationis*. The other conspicuous insects of the blanket mires are the dragonflies, small boggy pools and flushes supporting populations of black darter *Sympetrum danae*, common hawker *Aeshna juncea* and keeled skimmer *Orthetrum coerulescens* along with a few common species of damselfly.

The Welsh Peatland Invertebrate Survey investigated a few of the Region's upland mires in 1989 and collected information on the less obvious members of the fauna. Their most outstanding discovery in this habitat was the previously unsuspected presence of the ground beetle *Trechus rivularis*. This was considered to be a relict species of high-grade lowland fens in eastern England but it was shown to be reasonably common at high altitude on Migneint and also in Powys on a remnant of Llanbrynmair Moors. It has subsequently been found in similar habitat on the Border Mires of Northumberland and may prove to be relatively widespread on undisturbed blanket mires. Other characteristic carabids occurring on Migneint and Berwyn were *Carabus glabratus*, *Calathus micropterus*, *Patrobus assimilis* and *Agonum ericeti*. The scirtid beetles *Cyphon kongsbergensis* and *C. punctipennis* and the leiodid beetle *Agathidium convexum* were other

scarce species encountered during the survey which appear to be strongly associated with undisturbed *Sphagnum* mires in the uplands.

A typical, though nationally uncommon, spider of upland mires is *Clubiona norvegica*, found on Berwyn and Blaen-y-werglodd, a valley bog on Mynydd Hiraethog in Denbighshire. This block of land to the west of Llyn Brenig reservoir contains large areas of quality peatland. Nug, a headwater mire in the catchment of the Afon Alwen, has a population of *Agonum ericeti* and the rare shore bug *Micracanthia marginalis* is also present. The extensive blanket mire of Gors Maen Llwyd on the edge of Llyn Brenig is another excellent site, supporting many characteristic invertebrates and also the uncommon spider *Notioscopus sarcinatus*, which is otherwise only known in Wales from Berwyn.

In general, the Clwyd uplands are less well-known than their more spectacular counterparts in Gwynedd and surveys would be very interesting. Edaphic and climatic factors are very different on the Clwydian Range, for instance, and this will surely be reflected in the fauna. As mentioned earlier, the ground beetle *Cymindis vaporariorum* is recorded from this area but not further west. To the south it is known from Radnor Forest and it seems likely that it is an example of an upland species with a sub-oceanic distribution. The ground beetle *Trichocellus cognatus* is perhaps similarly distributed in Wales. Species from other beetle families and different invertebrate orders may well share this pattern of distribution. Documenting the upland fauna of North Wales is an immense task but it is clear from the foregoing that the Region has many interesting and important species that deserve greater attention. Many invertebrate zoologists do visit these mountain areas but few submit records of their fieldwork and it would be a great help to our understanding of the fauna if this situation was improved. If decisions are to be taken for the benefit of invertebrate conservation in the uplands then there has to be a much more substantial body of knowledge on the distribution and ecology of individual species and the community composition of different habitat types. The wildlife of this wonderful landscape may prosper in its remoteness but some species may also suffer from our ignorance of their needs. The fortunes of the rainbow leaf beetle, Ashworth's rustic and Weaver's wave are linked to our management of developments in the uplands. If these and other rarities are to thrive then we cannot take their existence for granted.

Dyfed – Powys: Notable sites for the conservation of invertebrates (see Appendix 1.)

SJ

SO

ST

79

72

Montgomery Canal (72)

81 River Wye

80

MONTGOMERYSHIRE

RADNORSHIRE

Gregynog
Great Wood

81 River Wye

Glasbury
Shingle Beds

68 Llandinam
Shingle Banks

38 Bailey Einon

77
Rhosgoch

63

Llangorse Lake
70

64

72

46 Coed Cnwch/Allt Ddu

Coed Aberedw 45

BRECONSHIRE

River Severn (79)

57

Doldowlodd
& Llysdinam
Estates

74
Nant Sere

River Usk (80)

36 Aberithon Turbary

River Wye (81)

Coed-y-cefn

48

73
Mynydd Illtyd

55 Cwm Llyfnant

79

81

Coed Mynachlog-fawr

River Usk
80

75

SH

SS

91 Ynys Eidiol

37

Ogof Ffynnon Ddu

SN

59 Dyfi Saltmarsh

47

Figyn Blaen-brefi

76 Rheidol Shingle
Banks

49
Cors Caron

61

Ynyslas 92

50

Cors Fochno

88
Tynbedw-grogwynion

CARDIGANSHIRE

Llanwrda Shingle Beds
71

Tanybwlch 87

65

89

Gwaun Garthenor
a Llanio-isaf

Ty'n-yr-helyg

Talley Lakes
86

CARMARTHENSHIRE

Ynys Uchaf
93

Bishop's Pond
41

51
Cors Goch Llanllwch

Rhos Llawr-cwrt
78

Afon Teifi (37)

Laugharne Burrows
66

90 West Williamston

39 Banc-y-mwldan
40 Banc-y-warren

54 Cwm Gwaun

67 Lawrenny Wood

52 Cors Penally

Creigiau Gwbert
53

Brynberian Moor
44

62
Freshwater East

85 Stackpole

Afon Teifi 37

Esgym
Bottom
60

PEMBROKESHIRE

43
Broomhill
Burrows

42
Bosherston Lake

Llangloffan Fen

69

St Davids
Head
82

58

Skomer
84

83

Dowrog Common

Skokholm
Island

SM

00

80

SR

N

kilometres

25

0

44

Dyfed-Powys Region

St Bride's Bay, Dyfed. [D.G. Jones]

Introduction

The area formerly administered by the Nature Conservancy Council (NCC) as Dyfed-Powys Region comprised 10,620 square kilometres of south-western and central Wales, covering just over half of the land surface area of Wales as a whole. As this overview is based on information collected prior to the formation of the Countryside Council for Wales, the discussion of sites and species of particular significance for invertebrate conservation in Dyfed-Powys refers to the pre-1991 NCC boundaries. This Region is composed of the two modern counties of Dyfed and Powys, with the exception of the Llanelli Borough of Dyfed which fell within NCC's South Wales Region. Subsequent to the formation of the Countryside Council for Wales there has been a change in regional boundaries such that Brecon Beacons National Park is now contained within South Wales Region and Llanelli Borough is part

of the Dyfed and Mid Wales Region. Dyfed-Powys is essentially rural and sparsely populated. Powys has fewer inhabitants per square kilometre than any other county in England and Wales. Farming and forestry account for an extremely high proportion of the land-use of the region and heavy industry is largely confined to the Milford Haven oil-terminals, the Ammanford area, and the extreme south of Brecknock District. In biological recording terms, Dyfed-Powys corresponds, more or less, to the Watsonian vice-counties of Carmarthenshire, Pembrokeshire, Cardiganshire, Montgomeryshire, Radnorshire and Breconshire, excluding the Llanelli Borough of Carmarthenshire and a small area of south Breconshire which was included in Gwent and Mid Glamorgan during the 1974 boundary revision.

The two major geological formations of the

Region are Silurian mudstones and Old Red Sandstone which, through the processes of glaciation, give rise to the rolling contours that are such a familiar feature of the upland landscape. The Silurian grits and shales, together with outcrops of the older rocks of the Ordovician era, predominate over most of the north and west of the Region and weather to produce rather acidic soils poor in nutrients. To the south and east, the Old Red Sandstone (which is mainly composed of sandstones and marls) tends to be lime-rich and yields more fertile soils which, with their higher mineral content, support vegetation typical of neutral or mildly calcareous substrates. A narrow band of Carboniferous Limestone outcrops from the southern tip of Pembrokeshire, through Carmarthenshire, and along the edge of the Brecon Beacons. There is also an isolated outcrop in the north-east of Montgomeryshire on the English border. Associated with the limestones are base-rich woodlands and grasslands, containing assemblages of plants and animals that are absent from the rest of the Region. Acid, intermediate and basic igneous rocks in western Pembrokeshire and the Coal Measures of the Amman Valley add further diversity to the Region's geology.

Deposits of boulder-clay, left behind in the wake of the glaciers, overlie the country rock in many places, particularly along the coast of Cardiganshire and north Pembrokeshire, southern Breconshire, and Carmarthenshire south of the Afon Tywi. The resultant heavy soils are generally poor-draining and give rise to wet mesotrophic pastures or woodlands dominated by ash and pedunculate oak. The last Ice Age also left a legacy of natural basins, in the form of pingos and kettleholes, which are scattered across the Region and which, nowadays, frequently contain well-developed acidic mire communities. As the glaciers retreated, peat began to form in suitable areas across much of Dyfed-Powys and continues to accumulate under the influence of the high rainfall which affects all but the eastern fringe of Powys in the rain-shadow of the Cambrian Mountains. Radio-carbon dating has determined that most peat-formation began in the period 6000-8000 years ago. Other geomorphological features of importance in Dyfed-Powys include the accumulations of wind-blown sand forming the major dune systems; the alluvial gravels of the river valleys which drain the Silurian shales; and the localised deposits of glacial sands, particularly those which blocked the outflow of the ancient lake of Llyn Teifi that is thought to have covered a vast area of central Dyfed.

Within this geological and geormorphological framework there are several habitat-types in Dyfed-Powys that contain sites of national importance for the conservation of invertebrates. Along the coast, pride of place goes to the major dune systems of Carmarthenshire and south Pembrokeshire, particularly Laugharne Burrows, Stackpole and Broomhill Burrows. They are of especial importance for their populations of several nationally rare species of bees and wasps, but also support a number of sand dune flies which have their strongest British colonies on the dunes of the south coast of Wales. There do not appear to be any outstanding examples amongst the Region's woodlands and the best sites for the dead wood fauna of over-mature trees are to be found on a few private estates in Montgomery, Radnor, and at Dinefwr in Carmarthenshire. The ancient trees of the deer park at Dinefwr have an assemblage of beetles that puts it amongst the top national sites for the saproxylic fauna of pasture-woodlands. An interesting inhabitant of the Radnorshire woodlands is the longhorn beetle *Pyrrhidium sanguineum*, which breeds in the branches of old oaks and has its British headquarters in this part of the Region.

Unimproved grasslands are still reasonably widespread in Dyfed-Powys and there are many fine colonies of marsh fritillaries *Eurodryas aurinia* on the horse- or cattle-grazed pastures of Dyfed in particular. It is difficult to select individual grassland sites of importance as it is the continued presence of a network of suitable habitat that contributes to the richness of the fauna and reduces the chances of localised extinctions becoming permanent. The same is true of the lowland heaths and fens of the Pembrokeshire Commons, where the large expanses of similar habitat in close proximity to each other ensure that the more mobile invertebrates can find suitable breeding conditions on nearby sites if management (or its neglect) changes the structure of the habitat on their existing sites. A speciality of these Commons, which is dependent upon management maintaining open flushes, is the southern damselfly *Coenagrion mercuriale*. The colonies here support stronger populations than occur anywhere else in Britain outside the New Forest.

There can be no doubting that the two raised mire National Nature Reserves of Cors Fochno and Cors Caron are amongst the top national sites for invertebrate conservation. There are few large raised mires in England and Wales with an intact hydrology and both of these sites support a distinctive fauna associated with such habitats. Foremost among the rare species is the rosy marsh moth *Eugraphe subrosea*, which was discovered on Cors Fochno more than a hundred years after its disappearance from the Cambridgeshire Fens. Peatlands are well-represented in the Region but natural lakes are scarce and few are of major significance for invertebrates. Bosherston Lake, however, supports several scarce aquatic invertebrates and Llangorse still has potential as an important site despite problems with eutrophication in the past. The freshwater resource of greatest value for invertebrate conservation in Dyfed-Powys is the countless streams and rivers that drain the uplands. The clear waters of the Severn, Wye, Teifi and others are home to many scarce aquatic invertebrates, including an exceptional diversity of mayflies and caddisflies. Linked with the major rivers are substantial shingle deposits that are clearly of national importance for their highly-specialised fauna, particularly ground beetles, rove beetles and spiders.

It is perhaps understandable that, in a Region with so few resident invertebrate specialists, most attention has been paid historically to the fauna of the richer and more accessible lowlands. Although there have been a small number of naturalists in Dyfed-Powys with broader interests, knowledge of invertebrate distribution was largely confined to the Lepidoptera until after the Second World War. There are rare instances of visiting specialists producing lists for other invertebrate orders in the early part of the century, particularly for the Pembrokeshire islands which have long held a fascination for entomologists, but it was really only with the appearance of the journal *Nature in Wales* in 1955 that resident naturalists began to display an interest in the lesser-known groups. Nonetheless, the scarcity of naturalists in general throughout the Principality meant that the task of cataloguing the invertebrate fauna and identifying sites of significance for their conservation was always an uphill struggle. In 1971, in recognition of this problem, a Biological Recording Group for Wales was formed under the auspices of the National Museum of Wales to enhance all aspects of natural history recording but with a particular emphasis on invertebrates. Sadly, this initiative only lasted a few years but it coincided to some extent with a growing awareness amongst the conservation organisations that the needs of invertebrates had to be catered for alongside the birds, mammals and flowers.

In such a sparsely populated Region with such a wealth of potentially interesting habitats there is always going to be a shortage of invertebrate zoologists and it will always be possible for the visiting specialist (or novice) to make a valuable contribution to regional knowledge of invertebrates. However, there are increasing signs that the principles of invertebrate conservation are gaining recognition and the management of reserves is now generally geared towards the whole ecology of a habitat rather than to a few of its more conspicuous species. There is, for example, a more enlightened approach to woodland management, to grazing intensity on flower-rich pastures, and to the maintenance of lowland heathland with a varied vegetation structure. On the survey side, there are an increasing number of site-based projects for the identification of the major components of the fauna; several groups such as dragonflies, moths and snails are being mapped on a county-wide basis; and small-scale autecological studies are being undertaken on several of the rarer invertebrates of the Region. In recent years, the Dyfed Invertebrate Group has sought to co-ordinate the survey efforts of entomologists in the vice-counties of Carmarthenshire, Pembrokeshire and Cardiganshire and to maintain links with its far-flung members through the regular production of its Newsletter. In Powys, however, there is an even greater lack of resident entomologists and, for instance, it is likely that Montgomeryshire is a strong candidate for the most under-worked vice-county in England or Wales. On a broader scale, the NCC's Welsh Peatland Invertebrate Survey sampled over a hundred of the best peatland sites in Wales (the first major entomological survey in the Principality) and a high proportion of these sites are located in Dyfed-Powys. The Region has a vast potential for invertebrate conservation in its varied landscape, a potential which can only be realised if the current upsurge of interest is maintained.

Coastlands

Black Scar, Dyfed. [A.P. Fowles]

The mainland coastline of Dyfed extends for more than 300 km from the Dyfi estuary in the north to Kidweli in the south. Hard rock cliffs occupy much of its length but this varied and little-modified coast also includes major dune systems, extensive saltmarshes, shingle beaches and boulder-clay cliffs. In addition, the islands of the south-west provide grassland and cliff habitats with faunas characteristically depauperate as a result of their isolation but nonetheless containing a high proportion of nationally scarce species. The prevailing geology of the northern coast offers little variation in rock-type but the remaining coastline to the south and east of Strumble Head has a complex structure including limestones, Old Red Sandstone and igneous rocks. Mild winters and the southerly aspect of much of the coastal fringe permits the occurrence of a range of warmth-loving invertebrates, whilst the relatively high rainfall contributes to the abundance of cliff seepages and flushes inhabited by a distinctive and specialised fauna.

Intertidal regions support a limited range of invertebrates that can tolerate the high salinity of such habitats. Estuarine mudflats are a typical example where low species-diversity is complemented by an extraordinary density of individuals, in the order of tens of thousands of molluscs, copepods, amphipods, etc. per square metre. Higher up on the saltmarsh, amongst the pioneer communities of glasswort, terrestrial invertebrates such as beetles, spiders and flies begin to appear, many species being restricted to short bursts of activity between the tides and then retreating to air-pockets within burrows, crevices, or mats of vegetation as water levels rise; the burrowing species typically occurring in well-drained aerobic sediments with a sparse cover of plants. Many of the estuaries in West Wales are affected by the invasion of cord-grass and this can be expected to alter the distribution of invertebrates on the lower saltmarsh as the patterns of sediment deposition are changed. The more stable upper saltmarsh has a richer fauna which varies in response to vegetational structure, the nature of the substrate, and the preponderance of areas of bare sediment. Most Dyfed saltmarshes are ungrazed, hence enabling

48

Sabra harpagula (Lepidoptera): Restricted to the woodlands of the Wye Valley, where the caterpillars feed on small-leaved lime, the scarce hook-tip is one of our rarest and most beautiful moths. (Photograph by J. Porter.)

Wye Valley, Gwent: The spectacular gorge woodlands of the Wye Valley are composed of a mixture of different tree species. Small-leaved lime is common in many parts of the valley. (Photograph by A.P. Fowles.)

Trichius fasciatus (Coleoptera): The bee chafer breeds in dead wood and the adults can be seen visiting flowers in summer. It is a fairly widespread species in Wales but the adults are rarely abundant. (Photograph by S.G. Ball.)

Pembrey Forest, Dyfed: Broad, sunny rides through this conifer plantation support a surprisingly rich fauna on the remnants of dune grassland along the track verges. Pembrey Forest is one of the best butterfly sites in Dyfed and is managed sympathetically for its wildlife. (Photograph by A.P. Fowles.)

South Stack, Anglesey: One of the best examples of coastal heath in Wales. Silver-studded blues *Plebejus argus* are abundant here, many of them breeding along the margins of sandy tracks.
(Photograph by A.P. Fowles.)

Dowrog Common, Dyfed: Lowland wet heath is best represented in Pembrokeshire where many large areas of common land support this distinctive type of habitat. Regular management is required to maintain a variety of stages in the heathland succession.
(Photograph by A.P. Fowles.)

Welsh Moor, Gower: Traditional grazing patterns on the Gower commons sustain a mosaic of unimproved grassland, heaths and mires over large areas of the peninsula. Marsh fritillaries *Eurodryas aurinia* are frequent on many of the commons, although regular burning probably reduces the overall potential of grasslands for invertebrates.
(Photograph by A.P. Fowles.)

***Eurodryas aurinia* (Lepidoptera):** Approximately one-third of all British colonies of the marsh fritillary occur in Wales. Some of these are very strong, with several thousand adults emerging each year, but many others are small and threatened with extinction through habitat loss and mis-management.
(Photograph by P. Waring.)

rich faunas to survive, and the introduction of grazing stock would be regarded as detrimental. However, on sites where there is an established tradition of grazing, this should be maintained at existing low levels, particularly in transition zones where the encroachment of carr woodland can exclude species which favour open conditions.

There has been little investigation of the non-marine invertebrate communities of saltmarshes in Dyfed but characteristic ground beetles such as *Dicheirotrichus gustavi*, *Bembidion laterale*, *B. iricolor* and *B. minimum* have been recorded, whilst the saltmarsh wolf spider *Pardosa purbeckensis* is widespread and the linyphiids *Erigone longipalpis* and *Halorates reprobus* are frequently abundant. On the upper fringe, reached only by the highest spring tides, the short-winged conehead *Conocephalus dorsalis* is usually present, whereas the much rarer Roesel's bush cricket *Metrioptera roeseli* is restricted to the perimeter of the Dyfi estuary where it inhabits rank grassland characterised by a dominance of sea club-rush. Ditches and seepages marking the transition between freshwater and brackish habitats are an important feature of the upper saltmarsh and support a range of Diptera, including hoverflies (e.g. *Platycheirus immarginatus* and *Tropidia scita*), soldier flies (e.g. *Oplodontha viridula*, *Nemotelus notatus* and *Stratiomys singularior*), craneflies, etc.

Above the littoral zone, strandlines provide shelter and humid conditions for invertebrates in a frequently hostile environment along with a rich supply of organic matter for detritivores and scavengers. Differences in the underlying substrates affect the fauna which can occur here but one of the chief factors contributing to a rich assemblage is the length of time that the piles of debris have remained undisturbed. For this reason, heaps of seaweed cast up by storms beyond the reach of normal tides yield the greatest diversity, particularly if the strandline is deep enough to remain internally moist through periods of hot weather. Sieving will reveal large numbers of beetles including *Cafius xantholoma*, *Ocypus ater* and *Cercyon littoralis*, along with many linyphiid spiders such as *Erigone arctica*. Diptera can be abundant in strandline debris and the local hoverfly *Eristalinus aeneus* is a characteristic species associated with rotting seaweed, as are members of the Coelopidae, Scatophagidae, Anthomyiidae and many other families. There is little information at present on the flies of Dyfed's strandlines but it is likely that the fauna is comparatively species-rich in a national context. Driftwood on sandy beaches shelters a range of species and localities with a

traditional abundance generally have a high invertebrate diversity. A typical species found under strandline timber is the smooth, black ground beetle *Broscus cephalotes*, which is widespread along the Dyfed coast. A more localised species, occurring on relatively undisturbed beaches, is *Nebria complanata*, a large black and yellow carabid which preys on marine talitrids (sandhoppers) and insect larvae. It is known from a few sites in the south of the Region and, in Britain, occurs elsewhere only along the shores of the Bristol Channel. Another rare species of sandy driftlines is the small, white woodlouse *Armadillidium album* which, although localised in distribution, can occur in vast numbers amongst seaweed and *Spartina* debris partially buried by sand on the uppermost strandlines.

Along the rocky shores of Dyfed, amongst the seaweeds and rock-pools, is another intertidal habitat with a distinctive and highly-specialised non-marine invertebrate fauna. The western seaboard is noted for its internationally important seabird colonies but it is not always appreciated that our rocky coasts are of considerable significance for those invertebrates which spend their lives in rock crevices exposed twice daily to the air. This fauna is at its most abundant and diverse in the upper bladderwrack *Fucus vesiculosus* zone in sheltered bays, particularly where there is a good supply of fine sediments. The rock strata of the Dyfed coast lends itself to the formation of crevices and here, in air-pockets, springtails and mites abound. A conspicuous species is the plump, blue-grey springtail *Anurida maritima* which occurs in discrete colonies and is preyed upon by specialist predators such as the pseudoscorpion *Neobisium maritimum* and the centipede *Hydroschendyla submarina*. Ubiquitous species include the rove beetle *Micralymma marina* and the centipede *Strigamia maritima*, whilst the tiny ground beetle *Aepus robini* is a notable, localised inhabitant known outside Britain only from the western coasts of southern Norway and northern France. Higher up the shore, rock-pools in the splash-zone are home to the water beetle *Ochthebius subinteger* and lichens are fed upon by larvae of the crane fly *Limonia unicolor*.

Above the shore, coastal cliffs support higher plant cover and an associated array of phytophagous invertebrates. Many species with broad habitat tolerances will occur if their relevant foodplants are present but there are also a number of species which are either restricted to the coastal fringe or are at least at their most abundant here. Lepidoptera are the most comprehensively surveyed group and the cliff habitats of Dyfed support a good range of

Pill woodlouse *Armadillidium album*.
[S. Hopkin]

nationally scarce species. Thrift is host to the thrift clearwing *Bembecia muscaeformis*; larvae of Barrett's marbled coronet *Hadena luteago barrettii* and the micro-moth *Caryocolum vicinella* eat the roots and leaves respectively of sea campion; and other locally uncommon species such as the feathered brindle *Aporophyla australis pascuea*, crescent dart *Agrotis trux lunigera* and northern rustic *Standfussiana lucernea* are polyphagous on low-growing plants and grasses. Butterflies favour the warmth of south- and west-facing cliffs, with healthy populations of grayling *Hipparchia semele* and dark green fritillary *Argynnis aglaja* widely distributed and small blues *Cupido minimus* occurring in discrete colonies on sheltered slopes with stands of kidney vetch. Phytophagous beetles also abound with the rich coastal flora, including the chrysomelid *Chrysolina banksi*, the scarce chafer *Amphimallon ochraceus* and weevils such as *Caenopsis waltoni*, *Trichosirocalus dawsoni* and the violet-feeding *Orobitis cyaneus*. Grazing helps to sustain plant diversity on the cliff grasslands and prevents red fescue and other grasses from smothering the sward. Many scarce species of coastal invertebrate prefer the short turf grasslands maintained by rabbits or domestic stock. As with other types of lowland pasture, cessation of grazing can have serious effects on the maritime invertebrate community and the re-instatement of moderate levels of grazing to the coastal cliffs of Dyfed should be widely encouraged.

High summer temperatures are the principal reason for the greater diversity of Orthoptera on coastal cliffs than any other type of habitat in the Region, with great green *Tettigonia viridissima*, grey *Platycleis albopunctata*, speckled *Leptophyes punctatissima* and dark *Pholidoptera griseoaptera*

bush crickets in cliff scrub and grassland, along with four species of common grasshoppers. The lesser cockroach *Ectobius panzeri* (a native species which lives under mats of low vegetation) occurs locally along the south coast of Dyfed. The favourable climate is also responsible for the wealth of bees and solitary wasps which breed in burrows along the cliff-top, where wind-blown sand and head deposits overlie the rock. Bees and wasps have declined considerably in Britain as a result of the loss of habitat and the Welsh coastal fauna is therefore regarded as being of national importance. Sites with a prolific source of nectar and plenty of available nesting habitat are rich in species, including national rarities such as *Andrena rosae*, *A. labiata* and *Mellita leporina*. Exposed patches of sandy drift deposits on top of the hard rock cliffs are used as nest-sites for burrowing species and even the edges of tracks and pathways can be important in this regard. Sharing similar micro-sites is the hoverfly *Eumerus sabulonum*, a coastal speciality which appears to favour bare ground along the edge of coastal footpaths on the cliffs. Another scarce invertebrate of friable soil micro-sites is the purse-web spider *Atypus affinis*. One of very few Welsh colonies of this extraordinary spider is established in boulder-clay mixed with sand on a south-facing slope at St David's Head in Pembrokeshire. The spiders live in burrows up to twenty-five centimetres deep, which they may occupy for as many as eight years.

An important feature of these western cliffs is the presence of flushes and seepages. In the wetter sites with marsh vegetation, particularly on boulder-clay, scarlet tiger moths *Callimorpha dominula* breed on water mint and soldier flies develop as larvae in saturated cushions of moss.

Dolichopodid and empid flies are also common but few sites have been studied for these groups as yet from such habitats within the Region. Craneflies, too, are well-represented on cliff flushes and they include *Gonomyia bradleyi* on the eastern bank of the Afon Teifi near its mouth; this is an extremely rare species nationally. Where there are grassy overhangs trickling with water the cranefly *Limonia goritiensis* is often present, whilst wet rock faces support the notable flies *Hercostomus chetifer* and *Clinocera nigra*. Seepages extending across gravel at the top of the beach, a feature which is well-developed at Freshwater East for instance, are inhabited by *Dolichopus signifer*, a nationally rare fly which has been found at several sites on the south Dyfed coast. Even the thin algal film of seepages over bare rock within the reach of salt-spray can support a specialised fauna, which includes the minute water beetle *Octhebius poweri*, known from Whitesand Bay and a handful of sites in Devon and Dorset.

Another important habitat provided by cliff localities is the talus zone of shattered rock and clay on the lower slopes above the storm beach. Many predators and scavengers from different invertebrate groups figure prominently here, including ground beetles, rove beetles and centipedes, but talus is of particular significance for several species of woodlice, some of which are restricted to the coastal fringe in Wales. *Armadillidium nasatum* and *Cylisticus convexus* can be found at the foot of the cliff and *Halophiloscia couchi* is widespread at the top of boulder beaches. Under moss and low mats of vegetation further up the slope, the pill woodlouse *Armadillidium pulchellum* is widely-distributed. Britain holds a significant proportion of the world population of this species, which is confined to north-western Europe.

Sand dunes are a distinctive coastal habitat with many special features of importance for invertebrates. Their well-drained substrate of sand grains heats up quickly in the high insolation of the coastal belt and is therefore favourable to species requiring high temperatures for development, especially those that occupy burrows as adults or larvae. Dunes are also an important formation for invertebrates as they contain a mosaic of conditions which have vanished from many inland sites as a result of land reclamation of one form or another; these conditions include a variable water-table, expanses of bare ground, unimproved grassland, and unpolluted water-bodies. Of additional significance in Dyfed-Powys is the presence of a relatively calcareous substrate, derived from marine shells and Foraminifera. There are several fine examples of dune systems in Dyfed and they are highly regarded for their invertebrate faunas. Sites such as Laugharne Burrows, Stackpole Warren, Broomhill Burrows and Ynyslas Dunes have been reasonably well-studied for their invertebrates and shown to contain many species with a restricted distribution both regionally and nationally.

The invertebrate interest is spread throughout the dune succession from the foreshore to mature carr beyond the fixed dunes, with an increase in the diversity of species and their overall abundance accompanying the increased stability of each zone. As a general principal, however, there is a tendency for a greater number of eurytopic (ubiquitous) species to dominate the fauna as the proportion of bare sand declines. Effectively, as plant cover and humus content increases the dunes come to resemble unimproved pasture and, whilst this undeniably has important, mainly phytophagous, elements amongst its invertebrate community, fewer psammophiles (sand-loving species) are present. Bare sand is free-draining and easily burrowed into and many typical dune species exploit these properties at some stage in their life-history, properties which are diminished by a tangle of plant roots and higher humus levels. A greater number of stenotopic (habitat-specific) species, therefore, is found in the earlier stages of dune succession than further inland. The Dyfed dunes, generally speaking, have an active sand-supply and hence embryo and 'yellow dunes' are well-represented in most systems, whilst high rabbit populations ensure that exposed sand still occurs within fixed-dune grassland.

Storm beaches and embryo dunes are a harsh environment, exposed to strong onshore winds and subject to continual change as wind and tide reshape the land. Few species are capable of surviving here but this is where to find specialist moths such as the sand dart *Agrotis ripae* and coast dart *Euxoa cursoria*, whose larvae feed on the pioneer plants sea rocket and sea sandwort. This area is also the haunt of the spectacular coastal tiger beetle *Cicindela maritima*, the colourful adults of which can be seen dashing around in search of prey, although breeding probably takes place on firmer sand where the larvae live in burrows. As marram grass builds the familiar profile of the yellow-dune zone, shelter, topography and reduced sand mobility contribute to the enhanced conditions for invertebrates. Marram tussocks contain their own miniature ecosystem, with springtails and mites in the layer of dead litter hunted by spiders and beetles, which are in turn predated or parasitised by solitary wasps, parasitic wasps and various flies. Shore wainscot *Mythimna litoralis* caterpillars feed on the leaves, the jumping spider *Marpissa nivoyi* spends much of its life hunting amongst the stems, and a great many other species find food and shelter amongst the framework of the marram tussock. Hollows in the yellow-dunes provide some respite from the prevailing winds. Robber flies are common predators found sheltering here, notably *Pamponerus germanicus* (for which the Welsh dunes are a major stronghold), *Philonicus albiceps* and *Dysmachus trigonus*. The therevids *Dialineura anilis* and *Thereva annulata* are other nationally uncommon flies that are well-represented in the yellow-dunes along Dyfed's coast. On the surface of the sand, spiders such as *Xerolycosa miniata* and *Arctosa perita* are active hunters and the ground beetle *Calathus mollis* is a characteristic inhabitant. A striking insect found on patches of bare sand is the black and red sand wasp *Ammophila sabulosa* which stocks its broodcells with caterpillars caught nearby. Firm, open sand is ideal for burrowing and dunes support large colonies of fossorial bees and wasps. The edges of paths or small blow-outs will be colonised by a host of species, including solitary bees of the genus *Andrena* and the widespread digger wasp *Mellinus arvensis*. The rare *Coelioxys mandibularis*, a parasite of leaf-cutter bees, has been found on Stackpole Warren in Pembrokeshire. It is in the yellow-dunes, too, that several handsome species of coreid bugs are found, many of them with a southerly distribution, examples being the spectacular red and black *Coryzus hyoscyami* which is chiefly associated with restharrow and the large spurge bug *Dicranocephalus agilis* which feeds on sea spurge.

At the edge of freshwater seepages flowing across bare sand, or temporary pools in dune slacks, the rove beetles *Bledius fergussoni* and *B. longulus* inhabit burrows where they feed on algae. They are predated by the ground beetles *Dyschirius politus* and *D. impunctipennis* (amongst others) and their presence can be revealed by splashing water over the damp sand, forcing the beetles to evacuate their burrows. Dolichopodid and empid flies are common in such locations, typical species being *Teuchophorus monacanthus* and *Stilpon nubilus*. Permanent dune pools are important for Odonata of mesotrophic waters and in Dyfed these include the emperor *Anax imperator*, hairy *Brachytron pratense* and scarce hawker *Aeshna mixta* dragonflies. The bushes of creeping willow which often cover the floor of seasonally-flooded dune slacks are fed upon by caterpillars of the Portland moth *Ochropleura praecox* and the handsome leaf beetle *Chrysomela populi*, and the catkins are an important nectar source (along with grey willow) for bees in spring.

The stable grey-dunes, with their sward of red fescue and colourful flora, naturally support the majority of the plant-feeders of the dune fauna. Lepidoptera are conspicuous members of this community and in summer the dune grassland swarms with cinnabar moths *Tyria jacobaea*, six-spot burnets *Zygaena filipendulae*, common blue butterflies *Polyommatus icarus*, graylings, dark green fritillaries, meadow browns *Maniola jurtina* and, on southern dunes, brown argus *Aricia agestis* and small blues. The floristic diversity leads to an abundance of phytophagous beetles, including weevils of the genus *Apion* and brightly coloured leaf beetles such as *Cryptocephalus aureolus*. Rose chafers *Cetonia aurata*, dune chafers *Anomala dubia* and sulphur beetles *Cteniopus sulphureus* add their brilliance to this insect spectacle. The carabids *Harpalus anxius* and *Amara lucida* are duneland ground beetles which feed largely on plant material. Snails, too, reach their greatest diversity on the stable dunes, amongst which the banded snail *Cepaea nemoralis* is the most noticeable but less common species include *Theba pisana*, *Cochlicella acuta* and *Helicella itala*. These benefit from the additional calcium in their diet with which to make their shells. These snails are preyed upon by the larvae of sciomyzids, the snail-killing flies, a widespread species being *Pherbellia cinerella*, whilst the Pembrokeshire dunes also have two national rarities, *P. knutsoni* and *Salticella fasciata*.

Islands have always held a fascination for entomologists and the nature reserve islands of south-western Dyfed have received their fair share of attention. Skokholm and Skomer have been the most intensively-studied and contain many scarce and interesting species amongst their fauna. Both islands support immense seabird colonies and large rabbit populations which, for centuries, have modified the flora and had considerable effects upon the invertebrate fauna. This is perhaps most obvious in the richness of the fauna associated with dung and carrion, both of which are in ever-present supply, and birds'nests. Species associated with these micro-habitats include the beetles *Trox scaber*, *Aphodius ictericus*, *Nicrophorus interruptus* and *Gnathoncus schmidti*. The coastal grassland and cliff vegetation of the islands support faunas typical of such habitats on the Dyfed coast but there are undoubtedly many species which have not been able to reach the islands from the mainland because of their limited powers of colonisation, an example being the brachypterous (short-winged) meadow grasshopper *Chorthippus parallelus*. Nonetheless, the islands contain a rich and varied fauna which is more or less free from the pressures of agriculture, tourism and industry (which threaten even the unspoilt coastline of mainland Dyfed) and buffered from the worst effects of wind-borne pollution by virtue of their isolation. Despite their size, they contain elements of most of the major coastal habitats of the Region and are justly regarded as being of importance for the conservation of invertebrates of the coastal fringe.

Woodlands

Parc Pont Faen, Dyfed. [A.P. Fowles]

A typical wood in the counties of Dyfed and Powys, sadly, is heavily grazed and composed largely of neglected sessile oak coppice with a closed canopy and an absence of wood-edge habitats. These woods support a limited invertebrate fauna, although some scarce species will still be able to persist, and generally their value to wildlife conservation is low. This neglect of Welsh woodlands is widely recognised and has led to the formation of a "Coed Cymru" initiative to restore management and bring vitality again to the woodland landscape. However, not all woods in the Region are in such disrepair and there are many fine examples of a broad range of woodland types under the care of such bodies as the Woodland Trust, National Trust and the local conservation organisations.

Sessile oakwoods predominate and important sites such as Coed Ty Canol, Coed Aberedw, Carn Gafallt, Allt Rhyd-y-groes, Coed Rheidol and Pengelli Forest maintain characteristic invertebrate faunas. Pasture-woodlands, with their ancient trees and abundant dead wood, are uncommon but Dinefwr Deer Park, Gregynog

Great Wood and Doldowlodd provide habitats for many species dependent on over-mature timber. The upland birch and alderwoods of the Brecon Beacons, such as Nant Sere, Cwm Llwch and Cwm Oergwm, are of great value as woods at higher altitudes are extremely scarce. In the lowlands there are several extensive areas of willow and alder carr supporting a rich fauna associated with woods growing in marshy situations — for example, Cathedine Common, Coed Garthenor, Llanerch Alder Carr, Mawnog Gwaunynog, Abergorlech and the fringe carrs of the major peatlands. Gorge and valley woods are often the least disturbed as they are frequently dangerous for domestic stock and present difficulties for timber extraction. Sites such as Cwm Llyfnant, Coed Gwenffrwd, Cwm Twrch, Pendugwm, Bailey Einon and Ciliau Dingle are just a few of the better known amongst the numerous wooded valleys of the Region. In addition, there are the dramatic wind-pruned, hanging oakwoods of the coastal cliffs, the herb-rich ashwoods of the Carboniferous Limestone belt, the oak-elm-ashwoods of the Old Red

Sandstone, and the native beechwoods of south Brecon, all of which have little information at present on their invertebrate interest. This is a reasonably well-wooded Region and only a small proportion of sites have been adequately surveyed by invertebrate zoologists, but the indications are that there are likely to be many woodlands of significance for invertebrate conservation.

To the casual observer, a woodland stroll can give a false impression of the phenomenal abundance of invertebrates living on and beneath the canopy and around the edges of our native woods. Superficially, there may be just a handful of butterflies flitting across the path and perhaps the pervasive hum of insects from the branches above, but, in fact, woodlands support an extraordinary range of species (several thousand in a good locality) which live out of sight of all but the inquisitive naturalist. It is sometimes difficult, therefore, to appreciate the invaluable role invertebrates play as primary consumers, pollinators, decomposers and prey for other animals in the forest ecosystem. The richness and diversity is due chiefly to the unparalleled spectrum of niches that native woodlands provide, in comparison with any of the other major habitat formations. This spectrum ranges from the humus-rich upper layers of the soil to the leafy expanses of the canopy, incorporating a vertical depth not encountered in other terrestrial habitats, and is enhanced by the processes of maturity and decay in individual trees (upwards of four hundred years for some of our oldest specimens) that far exceeds the life span of the shrubs and herbs of non-wooded habitats. Given that woodlands, by virtue of the complexity of their structure, naturally contain more niches for invertebrates to occupy, it is not surprising that they support such a diverse fauna, but there is also a historical reason for this wealth of species.

Before Britain became separated from mainland Europe as a result of rising sea-levels some 7,000 years ago, woodlands covered most of the land surface as the natural climax vegetation. The woodland fauna was therefore well-established long before Man began clearing the forests to open up new habitats for primitive agriculture. Many European species of plants and animals that could have survived in these new grasslands, heathlands, etc. were denied subsequent colonisation by the considerable barrier of the English Channel. Since then, many spectacular inhabitants of the British forests have disappeared through Man's persecution, the wolf and the wild boar for example, but a far greater number of species of invertebrates must have become extinct as a result of his rapacious use of woodlands, and, in particular, the disruption of the natural

cycles of regeneration and decay that we recognise today as valuable signs of the health of our woodland wildlife. In the ancient forests, these natural cycles ensured a constant supply of niches for invertebrates but, with fragmentation of our wooded landscape, many woods are now too small to provide the full range of opportunities. Management must, therefore, cater to the strengths of existing micro-habitats within each wood, whilst seeking to enhance other important features wherever possible. It is beyond the scope of this account to do more than to describe a few of the major aspects of woodlands in Dyfed-Powys which are of significance for invertebrates. Practically every conceivable situation has its own specialised association of species and woodland managers must try to ensure that their activities do not unnecessarily interrupt the continuity of valuable micro-habitats within each site.

The most conspicuous and well-known invertebrates of woodlands are the butterflies, represented largely by the fritillaries and hairstreaks. There has been a contraction of range for high brown *Argynnis adippe* and pearl-bordered *Boloria euphrosyne* fritillaries within the Region, although they still cling on in a few localities, but the larger woods, free from grazing and with sunny rides or clearings, frequently support colonies of silver-washed fritillaries *A. paphia*, purple hairstreaks *Quercusia quercus* and commas *Polygonia c-album*. Brown hairstreaks *Thecla betulae*, too, are probably widespread where there are adjacent blackthorn thickets, although this is an elusive species which is most easily located during the winter in the egg-stage amongst the twigs of recent growth. Another elusive species is the white-letter hairstreak *Satyrium w-album*, undoubtedly affected by the spread of Dutch Elm Disease (along with many other invertebrates associated with elm), which hangs on in a few of the valley woodlands and other areas where wych elms survive. The hairstreaks receive most of their nourishment as adults from aphid 'honey-dew' on the surface of leaves in the canopy but the other woodland butterflies require flower-rich areas for nectar, as do many woodland insects. Indeed, large clearings, broad rides, or adjacent unimproved pastures and meadows are integral components of a healthy woodland and without such areas the woodland invertebrate fauna will be severely impoverished. Phytophagous species amongst the beetles, bugs and Lepidoptera, for instance, are often restricted to wood-edge habitats and will decline in sites which have become overshaded through a neglect of management. For many species, foodplants have to be growing in warm, sunny situations before breeding will take place and the richest woods for invertebrates contain elements of other habitat types within their boundaries or within easy reach nearby.

Nectar sources in glades or sheltered positions along rides or woodland margins will attract butterflies and moths, a wide range of flies, bees and wasps, and many species of beetle. In the spring and early summer, sallow catkins, blackthorn blossom, rowan and hawthorn are important whilst later in the year umbellifers and ivy flowers are amongst the most productive for insects such as hoverflies, longhorn beetles and solitary bees. Blackthorn flowers are particularly attractive to the large bumblebee-mimicking hoverfly *Criorhina ranunculi* (which has been found at several localities in the Region) and the less-distinguished *Platycheirus ambiguus*, both of which are nationally scarce. The woodland hoverfly fauna has been fairly well surveyed in Dyfed-Powys and includes a number of localised species, particularly in the larger, mature woodlands. Amongst the notable species recorded are *Rhingia rostrata*, *Callicera aenea*, *Brachypalpoides lenta*, *Xylota xanthocnema* and *Xanthandrus comtus*. In early summer the lusher, southern woodlands are graced by the handsome, bright-red, cardinal beetles *Pyrochroa coccinea* and *P. serraticornis* whereas the rarest member of this family, *Schizotus pectinicornis*, occurs in a few of the older woodlands of Radnor and Brecon. Hawthorns are an important nectar source at this time of year for longhorn beetles after they emerge from their long larval development in dead timber. *Judolia cerambyciformis* is a frequent visitor to hawthorn flowers in suitable woodlands, as are the two common *Rhagium* species (*mordax* and *bifasciatum*), *Strangalia*

maculata, *Grammoptera ruficornis* and, again in the Radnor woods, the rare *Pyrrhidium sanguineum*. Flower-rich woodland rides are the favourite haunts of predatory flies such as *Dioctria oelandica* and here the parasitic conopid flies of the genera *Conops* and *Myopa* sit in ambush, awaiting the appearance of bees and wasps on which to lay their eggs.

Shady, humid woodlands, a common feature of the numerous narrow valleys of the Region, support a different fauna to the more open, lowland woods. Here, species that require a moist, stable environment thrive amidst the mossy boughs and fern-clad branches or breed within the profusion of autumn fungi. Molluscs are typical inhabitants of the damper woods and several sites contain more than forty terrestrial species. Undisturbed sites have a full complement of molluscs recognised as ancient woodland indicators, such as *Acicula fusca*, *Leiostyla anglica*, *Phenacolimax major*, *Spermodea lamellata*, *Zenobiella subrufescens*, *Limax cinereoniger* and *L. tenellus*. Whereas the majority of these slugs and snails have a restricted distribution over most of England, the wetter and milder climate of western Wales permits several of them to occur in secondary woodland or more open habitats. Current evidence suggests that only *S. lamellata* and *L. tenellus* can be regarded as reliable indicators of ancient woodland in Dyfed and Powys. The snails have their attendant predators in the form of the ubiquitous beetles *Cychrus caraboides* and *Silpha atrata*, the flies *Tetanura pallidiventris* and *Pherbellia albocostata*, or the tiny harvestman *Anelasmocephalus cambridgei*. Flushes in the valleyside woodlands, often marked out by bands of ash and carpets of opposite-leaved golden saxifrage, have concentrations of the

Cone-headed fly *Myopa testacea*.
[S.G. Ball]

scarcer molluscs and they also support a large number of Diptera, best typified by the craneflies, that breed in moist woodland conditions, e.g. *Lipsothrix nervosa*, *Scleroprocta sororcula* and *Gonomyia limbata*.

Fungi prosper in these dank valleys and are fed upon by the adults, and/or larvae, of various beetles and flies. It can be expected that the fungus fauna will include several national rarities although at present this aspect of woodland invertebrates is poorly-known in the Region. The variety and abundance of fungi in the damp Welsh woods is likely to support good populations of fungus gnats (Mycetophilidae) along with other fungus-feeding dipteran families. Beetles occurring on or in fungi here include the black and orange *Scaphidium quadrimaculatum* and widespread staphylinids such as *Bolitochara obliqua*. The rarer *Thymalus limbatus* (Peltidae) feeds on fungal hyphae beneath the loosened bark of ancient trees in a few of the larger oakwoods. Even mildew growing on the underside of sycamore leaves is grazed by the attractive orange ladybird *Halyzia 16-guttata*. Other features of the valley woodlands, streams and waterfalls for instance, also have their own specialised faunas and the undisturbed character of such woods generally means that there is a wide range of available micro-habitats for invertebrates, contributing to a rich and diverse fauna.

Of course, each individual tree provides countless niches for invertebrates throughout its life and subsequent decay. There is the foliage itself, devoured by the caterpillars of hundreds of species of moths; the heartwood-feeding beetle larvae; twigs forming a framework for spiders' webs; and numerous cavities and depressions inhabited by the larvae of flies. Roots and rot holes, bark and its fissures, sap runs and epiphytes, all support different species that find shelter, food or moisture in their chosen site. As a tree matures the number of possible niches increases naturally with its growing stature and hence the older trees are highly-valued for invertebrate conservation. Few species are capable of feeding on living, healthy timber but as parts of the tree begin to die, either from natural senescence or damage, a succession of invertebrates can gain nourishment from the rotting fibres and therefore trees in some stage of decay contain a greater richness of invertebrates than younger, undamaged specimens. For this reason, ancient maiden or pollard trees are considered to be of the greatest significance for the conservation of woodland invertebrates, continuing to supply food for the leaf-eaters and becoming increasingly important for the inhabitants of dead wood. Whilst there are

hundreds of semi-natural woodlands classified as ancient in Dyfed-Powys, a high proportion consist of coppice-regrowth originating from stools that were clear-felled this century, chiefly for timber during the two World Wars. The only areas with trees more than a couple of hundred years old tend to be found on the large, private estates and there are very few good examples of these in the Region. The best sites, at Gregynog, Dinefwr and Doldowlodd, all correspond to the habitat-type known as wood-pasture and consist mainly of oaks that are probably 200-300 years old. The grazing of deer and sheep beneath the trees limits regeneration and seriously depletes the availability of nectar sources but, nonetheless, a valuable fauna is associated with each of these localities which sympathetic management could considerably enhance. Grazing also affects the quality of the dead wood fauna of fallen timber by reducing the extent of the field and shrub layers which protect logs and branches on the ground from desiccation. Dead wood rapidly dries out if it is fully exposed and becomes less acceptable to the majority of the specialised inhabitants (although certain bees and wasps will nest in old, sun-baked, beetle burrows).

Knowledge of the dead wood fauna of Dyfed-Powys is scanty at present but, where there is an abundant supply of dead and dying timber, several species which are scarce nationally have been recorded. Dinefwr Deer Park is the best known of the pasture-woodlands and here beetles such as *Conopalpus testaceus*, *Orchesia undulata*, *Thymalus limbatus*, *Platypus cylindrus*, *Stenagostus rhombeus* and *Prionus coriarius* can be found. Other saproxylic insects (species associated with dead or dying wood) known from the Region include the flies *Xylophagus ater*, *Sphegina verecunda*, *Ctenophora atrata* and *C. pectinicornis* and the beetles *Pediacus dermestoides*, *Xyloterus signatus*, *Hylecoetus dermestoides*, *Ischnomera sanguinicollis* and *Trichius fasciatus*. The curious larvae of the beetle *Ctesias serra* live on debris and remains caught in spiders' webs hidden beneath the bark of standing trees, most frequently in the cribellate webs (made from very fine strands of non-sticky silk) of *Amaurobius fenestralis*. *Segestria senoculata* is another widespread spider which often lives under bark; less common is the tiny linyphiid *Thyreosthenius parasiticus* which builds its webs in the dark centre of hollow trees.

Lichens proliferate in the clean, humid air of mid and west Wales and there are several woods in Dyfed and Powys with nationally important corticolous (growing on bark) lichen floras. The caterpillars of several species of moth feed on lichens in such situations and the Region has good populations of the dotted carpet *Alcis jubata*, Brussels lace *Cleorodes lichenaria*, red-necked footman *Atolmis rubricollis* etc. which are scarce in other areas affected by sulphur emissions from industrial air pollution. The oakwood defoliators, winter moth *Operophtera brumata*, mottled umber *Erannis defoliaria*, and green oak tortrix *Tortrix viridana*, are the most conspicuous caterpillars, providing food for the nestlings of woodland birds such as pied flycatchers and redstarts. No exceptionally rare moths have been reliably reported so far from woodlands in the Region but there is an assemblage of interesting species, including small brindled beauty *Apocheima hispidaria*, black arches *Lymantria monacha*, merveille-du-jour *Dichonia aprilina*, cloaked carpet *Euphyia biangulata* and double-line *Mythimna turca*, that occur widely in the better, ungrazed woods. Preying on caterpillars in the older oakwoods is the large, brassy ground beetle *Calosoma inquisitor* that climbs trees in search of food, although it is rarely seen because of this arboreal behaviour. The lichen-clad trunks and branches are the haunts of another predator, the oak bush cricket *Meconema thalassinum*, which is not uncommon but easily overlooked unless specifically searched for because of its nocturnal habits.

Predators abound, too, amidst the leaf-litter on the woodland floor, where millions of invertebrates decompose the phenomenal biomass that falls from the canopy each autumn, returning the nutrients to the soil to be taken up by the trees and shrubs once again. Amongst this rich mulch of decaying matter many invertebrates find food and shelter, including canopy species that over-winter here. Millipedes are major decomposers of the leaf-litter and *Chordeuma proximum* has its British stronghold in these acid oakwoods. In woods on richer soils the pill millipede *Glomeris marginata* is widespread and damp sites have the uncommon *Cylindroiulus londinensis* and *Craspedosoma rawlinsii*, which have so far only been found in ancient woodlands in the Region and may be tentatively regarded as indicator species for such woods in Dyfed and Powys. The masses of springtails, mites, flies and other insects in the litter-layer are preyed upon by spiders and ground beetles. In spring, the wolf spider *Pardosa lugubris* patters over the leaf surface in vast numbers and amongst the spaces between the leaves numerous money spiders lie in wait in their tiny webs. A rarity, known from just a few woods and wet heaths in South and West Wales, is the harvestman *Sabacon viscayanum* which is found elsewhere in Europe at only a few scattered localities around the Pyrenees. Typical woodland carabids include *Abax parallelepipedus*, *Calathus piceus* and, the mainly bark-dwelling, *Bembidion harpaloides*, whilst *Notiophilus rufipes* and *Pterostichus oblongopunctatus* are more localised ground-active hunters. In some districts, valley woodlands provide winter shelter for *Pterostichus aethiops*, escaping from the harsh climate of its summer home on the upland moors.

The movement of invertebrates, particularly insects, from open-ground habitats into woodlands during the winter highlights the important point, made earlier in connection with nectar sources, that woodlands are richer places for wildlife if there is a juxtaposition of various habitat-types. Mosaics of grassland, marsh or moor occurring within and alongside woods are of the greatest significance for invertebrate conservation. There is a two-way process in which woodland inhabitants benefit from adjacent semi-natural habitats, and vice versa. Nectar-feeding adults breeding within the wood fly out to visit meadow flowers; beetles and flies may use the larger flower heads of umbellifers etc. for courtship sites; female dragonflies elude the frantic bustle over ponds and rivers to hunt out prey and develop to sexual maturity along the wood-edge, whilst beetles and moths from the bleak, open country escape the rigours of winter by seeking out over-wintering sites in the equable woodland environment. The isolation of woodlands that diminishes their importance over much of central and southern England is less prevalent in Wales and the conservation of composite sites, in recognition of their enhanced value to the woodland ecology, will ensure that the woods of Dyfed and Powys maintain their rich and varied fauna.

Lowland grasslands

Rhos Bwlch-y-rhandir, Dyfed. [A.P. Fowles]

Within the largely pastoral agriculture of Dyfed-Powys, unimproved lowland grasslands have survived at a relatively higher density than in many parts of England and Wales. Despite the acceleration of grant-aided drainage and re-seeding in recent years, some areas of the Region have retained a high proportion of traditionally-managed pastures and meadows of significance for nature conservation. This is reflected in the fact that there are over seventy localities which have been designated as Sites of Special Scientific Interest to represent the wealth and variation of lowland grasslands in the Region. The majority of herb-rich grasslands are permanent pastures with moderate levels of grazing, although there are also a number of meadows at higher altitudes which are recognised as being nationally important for their distinctive flora. Variation is added by environmental factors such as the underlying geology, topography, site wetness and management history.

The commonest type of unimproved grassland in this part of Wales is wet, acidic pasture with a predominance of sedges and an abundance of purple moor-grass in the sward. In the south-east of the area, around the Ammanford district, the Carmarthen Coalfield has large expanses of such pasture, characterised by the presence of whorled caraway as a major component of the flora. Small-holdings were a side-line for the miners here and the fields were often only used as tack-grazing for a pony or two. This form of management created acres of herb-rich pasture of great value for wildlife and supported a rich diversity of flowering plants on the weakly acidic soils. Typical species would be greater burnet, meadow thistle, dyer's greenweed and a variety of orchids. Sadly, the closure of so many of the mines has led to the demise of this traditional management and, in addition, open-casting for coal now threatens much of this extremely valuable habitat. In the north of Carmarthenshire and over much of Cardiganshire, the typical pasture is really a mosaic of flushes, small mires, and sedge-rich grassland. These are known as 'rhosydd' (singular: 'rhos') and are often a sea of blue in late summer from the flowers of devil's-bit scabious amongst the purple moor-grass and rushes. A conspicuous feature is the widespread presence of the ericaceous species heather and cross-leaved heath amongst the grassland, both of which are kept short by grazing. These 'rhos' sites are frequently associated with periglacial features such as pingos (glacial hollows formed by ice-mounds), which create a suitable topography of banks and depressions for the assortment of plant communities characteristic of 'rhos' sites.

Mesotrophic, neutral grasslands are less common in the Region as a whole and usually occur where boulder-clay or alluvial deposits overlie the bedrock. Sweet vernal-grass is a frequent dominant, with showy herbs such as knapweed and oxeye daisy adding colour to the sward. In Pembrokeshire, where few lowland grasslands have escaped improvement (the extensive areas of common land have plant communities approximating more closely to wet heath), the 2500 ha MoD Castlemartin Range contains the largest area of neutral grassland in Wales, established on fields which were under arable cultivation until the early 1940s. Calcareous grasslands are even scarcer and lowland examples are largely restricted to the narrow bands of limestone running through Carmarthenshire and Radnorshire. Around 300 metres above sea level in most of the vice-counties (but particularly in Powys) there are still a few meadows managed for hay in favourable seasons and they are characterised by the presence of such nationally uncommon plants as globeflower, wood bitter-vetch and greater butterfly orchid.

Considering the extent and unquestioned importance of lowland grasslands in Dyfed-Powys it is rather surprising that these habitats have attracted little attention from invertebrate specialists and information has arisen largely from casual recording of the conspicuous members of the fauna, chiefly butterflies and moths. However, recent survey work on a few selected sites has demonstrated the entomological richness of unimproved grasslands in the Region and it may well transpire that the pastures of Dyfed and Powys comprise the national stronghold for a whole suite of species that have declined elsewhere in Britain in the face of increasing agricultural improvements. The marsh fritillary *Eurodryas aurinia* typifies this position, with about 20% of its known British colonies located in south-west Wales and several of these colonies support huge populations. At Rhos Llawr-cwrt NNR, for instance, population studies in 1984 estimated that 10,000 adults emerged during the season over the twenty-three hectares of suitable grassland. The ecological requirements of this notable butterfly (which is threatened

throughout most of its European range) incorporate several of the major features of conservation for invertebrates on the wet, acidic pastures — an abundance of the larval foodplant (devil's-bit scabious), good nectar sources for the rather sedentary adults, and the presence of a litter-layer over a fair proportion of the site to maintain a suitable micro-climate for the overwintering larvae. A patchwork of rank purple moor-grass and flower-rich turf is required to meet these conditions and it has been found that moderate grazing by horses or cattle (in the order of one pony per hectare) produces the necessary balanced mosaic.

This grazing regime also seems to favour a characteristic assemblage of scarce moths, many of them day-flying, including the silver hook *Eustrotia uncula*, forester *Adscita statices*, five-spot burnet *Zygaena trifolii*, chimney sweeper *Odezia atrata*, Devon carpet *Lampropteryx otregiata* and the 'micro-moths' *Olethreutes olivana* and *Aethes piercei*. Gaudy scarlet tigers *Callimorpha dominula* are widespread in such sites, particularly where there is a fringe of willow carr; in these situations the larvae mainly feed on water mint. Amongst the characteristic butterflies of these damp pastures are small pearl-bordered fritillaries *Boloria selene* (although they rarely occur in the woodland habitats favoured by this species in central and eastern England) and the ubiquitous ringlet *Aphantopus hyperantus*, meadow brown *Maniola jurtina*, small skipper *Thymelicus sylvestris* and large skipper *Ochlodes venata*. On the less-acidic wet pastures of the Carmarthen coalfield, marbled whites *Melanargia galathea* are widely distributed, often occurring in the same fields as the two fritillaries.

The lush vegetation of these pastures supports many species of hoverflies which can be found feeding at the abundant nectar-sources along with species which may breed in adjacent habitats but which visit these semi-natural grasslands to build up their energy reserves for reproduction. The handsome bee-mimic *Arctophila fulva* is a typical insect of such sites, the adults feeding at the flowers of devil's-bit scabious in late summer. Other hoverflies which can be more or less guaranteed to occur include *Helophilus pendulus, Rhingia campestris, Pyrophaena rosarum, Lejogaster metallina, Chrysotoxum bicinctum* and *Sericomyia silentis*. Several species of the genus *Eristalis* are abundant visitors to flowers, including the locally uncommon *E. abusivus* and, in a few localities, *E. rupium*, here near the southern limit of its British range. If searched for, the stem-boring larvae of *Cheilosia albipila* and *C. grossa* appear to be fairly common on pastures with marsh thistle, although the adults

The hoverfly *Sericomyia silentis*
[S.G. Ball]

themselves are rarely seen, particularly as they are on the wing in early spring. Many individual species of plants in these grasslands are hosts to specific insects. For example, devil's-bit scabious is an important source of food for a whole range of insects besides *Arctophila fulva* and marsh fritillaries: the larvae of the 'micro-moth' *Aethes piercei* feed on the rootstock while the leaves are devoured by several moths, the attractive sawfly *Abia sericea*, the tiny jewel beetle *Trachys troglodytes*, and the leaf beetle *Galeruca tanaceti*. An assortment of phytophagous beetles benefit from the floristic diversity of the wet pastures and scarce species recorded to date include *Chaetocnema arida*, *Hydrothassa glabra*, *Cassida murraea* and *Longitarsis holsaticus*.

Grazing is important to maintain the richness of the sward but the type of stock can also have a strong bearing on the constituents of the invertebrate fauna, both directly and indirectly. The damp, acidic pastures on the prevailing heavy soils of the Region are traditionally grazed by horses or cattle as the land is usually too wet for sheep. The larger animals graze the site unevenly if the stocking density is kept at a moderate level and this produces a natural mixture of pockets of rank grassland amongst open areas of shorter turf. The tussocks and litter-layer of the taller grasses provide ideal over-wintering sites for many species which would perish from exposure on the close-grazed sward. Purple moor-grass is ideal in this respect as the high silica content of its leaves prohibits rapid decompositon and the enduring framework of its litter gives winter-long protection for many frost-sensitive species. Alterations to the balance of grassland communites brought about by significant changes in the grazing regime, even

for a single year, can have adverse effects upon the invertebrate fauna and continuity of traditional forms of management is essential to maintain faunistic diversity.

Horses and cattle can also poach the ground in wet conditions and, whilst this is obviously not desirable on a large scale, localised poaching does open up bare ground and wet hollows for many species of flies to breed in. Damp soil is also ideal for the development of the larvae of tabanids, the familiar and troublesome horse flies. Dyfed-Powys has a good range of species from this family, many of which are declining in other parts of their range. *Chrysops viduatus*, *Atylotus fulvus*, *Tabanus cordiger* and *T. sudeticus* (one of the largest British flies but, fortunately, not known to bite Man) are still reasonably common in Wales and worthy of conservation, despite our initial reactions to their presence. The grazing animals also have their own attendant fauna associated with their dung, the ubiquitous yellow dung fly *Scathophaga stercoraria*, for instance, which breeds in cow-pats and its scarcer, western relative *S. scybalaria*.

The larvae of innumerable beetles and flies carry out the important task of breaking down dung and returning the nutrients to the soil and many of these species are specific to a particular type, or consistency, of dung; a factor which should be borne in mind before changes in the type of grazing stock are considered on grassland nature reserves. One of the most spectacular of all British flies, the black and orange hornet robber fly *Asilus crabroniformis*, is more or less dependent on cattle-grazed pastures where the larvae prey on the inhabitants of cow-dung. This beautiful insect occurs on a few of the neutral grasslands in the south of the region and, like many other members of the family Asilidae, is usually associated with lighter, free-draining soils. At present, grasslands of this type are under-worked entomologically but as they differ so significantly in character from the water-logged pastures they will undoubtedly prove to sustain a different, but nonetheless interesting, fauna. From the few available records it is apparent, for instance, that there are a number of uncommon weevils occurring here, such as *Larinus planus*, *Mogulones euphorbiae*, *Apion punctigerum* and *A. rubiginosum*.

One feature of the richer grasslands which has recently come under the spotlight in the Region is the spring-fed flush systems which occur quite widely on sloping pastures. Attention has been concentrated on the peaty flushes of Banc-y-mwldan in Cardiganshire where a strong colony of the green and black soldier fly *Odontomyia hydroleon* was recently discovered, a fly not previously recorded in Britain since about 1840. The flushes here originate from sand deposits associated with the glacial Llyn Teifi and the clear waters that emerge from springs below the deposits are strongly base-enriched. Subsequent investigations revealed the presence of other scarce soldier flies associated with these flushes, including *Oxycera rara*, *O. pygmaea* and *Oplodontha viridula*. Other interesting flies in this habitat are the dolichopodid *Syntormon pumilus* and the cranefly *Thaumastoptera calceata* and the notable ground beetle *Elaphrus uliginosus* is found on the bare peat flanking the flushes. Banc-y-mwldan is clearly a unique site because of its calcium-enriched springs but there are many

flushed grasslands in the Region which can be expected to support important faunas. Further survey work is required on all of the unimproved pastures of the Region, including the remaining sites of the Carboniferous Limestone belt. This is also true of the few surviving hay meadows where, apart from a few casual butterfly sightings, there is an almost total lack of information on the range of invertebrates present. Generally speaking, meadows are of reduced importance for invertebrates due to the sudden and dramatic changes in structure and micro-climate brought about by cutting for hay (or silage). However, the weather rarely allows the regular removal of a hay-crop and these grasslands are frequently grazed for several years before there is a suitable dry-spell in which to make hay. These sites are often at relatively high altitudes (around 250 metres a.s.l.) on heavy soils and it is quite likely that their fauna has some affinities with the damp pastures of lower altitudes.

The botanical richness of the lowland grassland habitats in Dyfed-Powys are prized as one of the Region's major contributions to nature conservation in Britain and there are indications that they could be of similar significance for their invertebrates. There is plenty of scope for adding to knowledge of the status and ecology of the grassland fauna in Dyfed-Powys and thereby enhance the sympathetic management of unimproved grasslands for their invertebrates as well as their flora.

Lowland heathlands

Dowrog Common, Dyfed. [A.P. Fowles]

Lowland heathlands in the Region are more or less confined to the county of Dyfed as heather-dominated habitats in Powys are only found on the high altitude moorlands. Five distinct types of lowland heath are found in Dyfed: the widespread coastal cliff-top heaths, the wet and humid heaths, the floodplain shingle heaths, dry heaths established on the spoil of abandoned lead-mines, and fragments of dry heath on rocky outcrops. Coastal heaths are still common in the three vice-counties of Dyfed although the twin pressures of natural erosion and agricultural improvement are gradually reducing the total extent of this valuable habitat. The plant communities are dominated by heather, bell heather and western gorse with a varying mixture of grasses and herbs, such as wood sage, betony and saw-wort. The pale blue flowers of spring squill are a notable feature of coastal heaths in the south-west of the region. Most of the wet and humid heaths occur in Pembrokeshire, particularly in the north and west of the district, and there are about a dozen small examples on the coastal plateau in Cardiganshire. Heather is once again the dominant plant species with much purple moor-grass, cross-leaved heath and western gorse. These heaths conform to the western Oceanic type of heathland and the maritime influence is strong enough on some of the Pembroke heaths to maintain sea plantain amongst the pioneer, open communities. Many nationally rare plants, including yellow centaury, three-lobed crowfoot and pale dog-violet, have strong populations on some of these sites. Shingle heaths have only recently been recognised in the Region and they appear to be restricted to the gravel-bed floodplain of the rivers Ystwyth and Rheidol in Cardiganshire, where there are half a dozen examples. Heather and purple moor-grass are the commonest flowering plants and there are usually mature bushes of common gorse scattered throughout the habitat. Much of the stony substrate is unvegetated or supports mats of saxicolous lichens, including several national rarities.

There are no true dry heaths of the kind occurring on sandy ground in southern England; in Dyfed the only lowland sites away from the coast where bell heather (a characteristic dry heath species in west Wales) is a prominent component of the vegetation are associated with rock outcrops, often of quartzite, in Pembrokeshire and Carmarthenshire. The soils here are very thin and do not generally favour the range of burrowing invertebrates so typical of the sandy heaths. At higher altitudes, around 250 metres above sea level, dry heath has colonised the spoil heaps of the lead-mines in North Cardiganshire since they were abandoned at the turn of the century. Their chief biological interest currently lies in the presence of a number of metallophytes (plants which are tolerant of high levels of heavy metal in the soil), including sea campion and alpine penny-cress, but entomological surveys could reveal the existence of a distinctive fauna associated with the friable substrate and large areas of open ground.

A narrow fringe of cliff-top heathland extends along much of the coastline of Dyfed. Exposure and erosion continually modify the plant communities in such habitats, resulting in a patchwork of heath and grassland with bare areas of slippage and pathways kept open by holidaymakers enjoying the splendid scenery of the coastal landscape. This intimate mixture of micro-habitats provides ideal conditions for species which favour the dry soils and/or the higher levels of sunshine. This is typified by the ants *Formica cunicularia* and *Tetramorium cespitum* which are regular inhabitants of the southern English heaths but in Dyfed-Powys are found mainly on the coastal heaths of Pembrokeshire. The robber fly *Leptarthrus brevirostris* is another characteristic species which requires open ground in warm places, although it is also found in a few inland localities. More obvious insects of the cliff-top heaths include grayling butterflies *Hipparchia semele*, mottled grasshoppers *Myrmeleotettix maculatus* and the large, ponderous, bloody-nosed beetles *Timarcha tenebricosa*. There is plenty of scope for further recording of most invertebrate groups (particularly the aculeate Hymenoptera which can be anticipated to be well-represented), and more rarities, like the tiger beetle *Cicindela germanica* found at Llanstephan or the click beetle *Cardiophorus erichsoni* known from the St David's peninsula, no doubt remain to be discovered.

The majority of inland heaths in the region are situated on waterlogged soils or shallow peats and are classified as wet or humid heaths. Besides heather-dominated vegetation they also contain mixtures of scrub, acidic grassland, small mires, pools and flushes and this mosaic of habitats supports a diverse invertebrate fauna of national importance. Many of the best examples of wet heath are on common land in Pembrokeshire and

two areas are of recognised importance for their dragonflies — the St David's peninsula commons and the lower slopes of Mynydd Preseli. The Preseli heaths are particularly significant for their strong colonies of the southern damselfly *Coenagrion mercuriale*, a rare species known otherwise from only a handful of sites outside its stronghold in the New Forest. Studies of the larval distribution have shown a dependence on shallow runnels crossing heathlands which are fairly heavily grazed, as trampling and grazing by stock maintains the open flush conditions necessary for larval development. The keeled skimmer *Orthetrum coerulescens* is another dragonfly which is common on the extensive flush systems of these wet heaths and where there is a stronger flow of water the beautiful demoiselle *Calopteryx virgo* and the golden-ringed dragonfly *Cordulegaster boltonii* are also present. Hollows filled with bog-mosses *Sphagnum* spp., and abandoned drains and peat-cuttings, are the breeding sites for the small red damselfly *Ceriagrion tenellum*, large numbers of which occur on Dowrog Common. Shallow heathland pools increase the dragonfly diversity, several sites supporting the scarce blue-tailed damselfly *Ischnura pumilio* for instance, and these pools can also be important for their water beetle fauna. Scarce beetles such as *Rhantus grapii* are known from a few localities in the Region and there are also old records of *Graptodytes flavipes* on the Pembrokeshire mainland, a rare species found on wet heaths mainly in southern England. *G. flavipes*, and the equally rare *G. bilineatus*, were both recorded on Skomer Island in the 1960s and might well occur in the heathland pools of the St David's peninsula.

Areas of bare or sparsely vegetated peat on boggy ground are used by egg-laying females from many families of flies, including members of the Ephydridae (shore flies) and Tipulidae (craneflies). The craneflies of these wet heath habitats, along with many other dipteran families, beetles, spiders, etc., have recently been surveyed by the Nature Conservancy Council's Welsh Peatland Invertebrate Survey. When these results are finally collated a clearer picture of the heathland fauna will be available, but it is already evident that a number of scarce craneflies are present on wet heaths in Dyfed, such as *Erioptera neilseni* and *Tipula melanoceros*. Bare drier ground along the trackways is a favoured haunt of the green tiger beetle *Cicindela campestris* and the pioneer stages of heathland support a number of characteristic ground beetles which search for their prey over relatively open ground. The large, bronzy *Carabus arvensis* is often found on heathlands, along with *Pterostichus versicolor*

Grogwynion, Dyfed: In a few places on the banks of rivers in mid Wales dry heath has developed on extensive shingle deposits. This is a rare habitat in Britain and its importance in Wales has only been recognised recently. Few invertebrate studies have been carried out but the fauna is known to include several species which are characteristic of the southern English heaths.
(Photograph by A.O. Chater.)

Rhos Glwydwern, Dyfed: The 'rhosydd' of south-west Wales are heathy grasslands on impeded soils with a sward dominated by purple moor-grass and various sedges. They are often associated with areas of periglacial activity and contain pools and basin fens which add to the range of habitats present on each site.
(Photograph by A.P. Fowles.)

Coenagrion mercuriale **(Odonata):** Mynydd Preseli in Pembrokeshire holds some of the best populations of the southern damselfly in Britain. It inhabits seepages and shallow runnels, favouring sites that are kept open by grazing.
(Photograph by Prema Photos.)

Brockwell's Meadow, Gwent: Flower-rich meadows in Gwent have all but vanished through agricultural improvement and the calcareous grassland of Brockwell's Meadow is one of the finest remaining examples. Marbled whites *Melanargia galathea* and great green bush crickets *Tettigonia viridissima* are southern species which are frequent here, though generally scarce in Wales. (Photograph by A.P. Fowles.)

Banc-y-mwldan: Base-rich flushes and seepages in unimproved pastures are becoming increasingly scarce. Many invertebrate species are restricted to such habitats, including a wide range of Diptera with semi-aquatic larvae. (Photograph by A.P. Fowles.)

Great Orme's Head, Gwynedd: The limestone grasslands of this spectacular coastal outcrop are best known for their populations of the endemic dwarf forms of grayling *Hipparchia semele* and silver-studded blue *Plebejus argus* butterflies. Grazing maintains a rich flora and prevents scrub from encroaching upon this important habitat. (Photograph by A.P. Fowles.)

***Callimorpha dominula* (Lepidoptera):** The scarlet tiger is a day-flying moth that inhabits wet pastures and fens in southern Wales. The Welsh colonies represent a stronghold for this species in Britain. (Photograph by P. Waring.)

Green tiger beetle *Cicindela campestris*
[R.S. Key]

and *Notiophilus germinyi*. Moister situations are preferred by *Pterostichus vernalis* and *P. diligens*, whilst *Leistus rufescens* is found where a deeper litter of heather and purple moor-grass maintains higher levels of humidity. There is a clear association, both in dry and wet habitats, between the carabids *Olisthopus rotundatus* and *Bradycellus ruficollis* (which are common inhabitants of Dyfed's heaths) and the presence of heather litter.

Many species of wolf spider are found on wet heathlands and the fauna typically includes *Pardosa pullata*, *P. palustris*, *Alopecosa pulverulenta* and *Pirata piraticus*. In the wettest areas *Pirata latitans* is a frequent member of the fauna, although this is an uncommon species nationally, and *P. piscatorius* has been found on a small number of the Pembrokeshire wet heaths. The *Sphagnum* and deep litter-layers are home to a great variety of money spiders that build their tiny sheet webs amongst the cover provided. As many as forty different species can occur in this habitat but most of these are also widespread on mires or fens where similar conditions of vegetation structure and humidity prevail. Two linyphiid species which are more readily found on wet heaths than peatland sites are *Walckenaeria vigilax* and *Kaestneria pullata*. Orb-weavers tend to require the more open architecture of heather and gorse as the heath matures and their webs can be a conspicuous feature from mid- to late summer. *Larinioides cornutus* and *Zygiella atrica* are commonest amongst the heather whilst *Metellina segmentata* and *Araneus diadematus*, for example, prefer to build their webs higher up in the gorse bushes.

Besides providing the framework in which so many species live, heather is also a foodplant for a variety of invertebrates. The heather beetle *Lochmaea suturalis* is the most notorious of these as it can occasionally reach plague proportions and defoliate large areas of heath, causing complete die-back of the heather. Fortunately this seems to be a rather rare event in West Wales. The larvae of the heather beetle are predated by the ladybird *Coccinella hieroglyphica* but this appears to be a rather localised species in Dyfed, occurring commonly on some sites but absent from other similar localities nearby. The most striking heather-feeder (although it also feeds on several other plants) is the large green and black caterpillar of the emperor moth *Saturnia pavonia* which eventually develops into an equally impressive adult with prominent eye-spots. This is a common insect of the Dyfed heaths but the adult moths are rarely seen at close quarters as the females are nocturnal and the diurnal males fly rapidly across the heaths in search of their mates. The northern eggar *Lasiocampa quercus callunae*, true lover's knot *Lycophotia porphyrea*, heath rustic *Xestia agathina* and beautiful yellow underwing *Anarta myrtilli* are amongst the other moths of Dyfed's heaths which are dependent on heather as a foodplant.

Silver-studded blues *Plebejus argus* have recently been rediscovered on the cliff-top heath and grassland of Castlemartin in Pembrokeshire and may be overlooked elsewhere. Apart from this species, none of our butterflies feed on heather. However, two species can be regarded as members of the heathland fauna — the grayling, which has already been mentioned in connection with the coastal heaths, and the green hairstreak *Callophrys rubi*. Gorse and broom are the principal foodplants of the latter on Dyfed heaths where the adults can be seen in early summer, flying around the tops of bushes or resting on the foliage. It is a widespread species but easily overlooked. Some of the wet heaths at the pioneer stage also support colonies of marsh fritillaries *Eurodryas aurinia*, although this is more usually an inhabitant of unimproved wet pastures in West Wales.

There appear to be few hoverflies which are characteristic of wet heaths, most species occurring widely in wetland habitats, but a notable exception is the nationally scarce *Microdon mutabilis*. It has been found at a handful of heathy localities in Dyfed where the larvae develop inside the nests of ants, feeding on their waste pellets. Several species of ants are known as hosts in Britain but on the wet heaths the most likely host is the abundant *Myrmica ruginodis*, or possibly the less frequent *M. scabrinodis*. Other hoverflies most often recorded on heathlands compared to other wetland habitats include *Sphaerophoria philanthus* and *Trichopsomyia flavitarsis*, but most of the hoverfly fauna is less selective. This is also the case with a high proportion of the invertebrate groups recorded on wet heaths in Dyfed, their individual character being defined more in terms of a distinctive assemblage of species rather than by the occurrence of a number of habitat-specific species. The work of the Welsh Peatland Invertebrate Survey, and a similar study organised by the Dyfed Wildlife Trust on Dowrog Common, will eventually yield a description of the invertebrate communities of wet heaths in Dyfed, encompassing a much broader range of species than can be mentioned here. For instance, initial results suggest that there is a characteristic hemipteran fauna, particularly amongst the leaf hoppers, with several national rarities including *Jassargus sursumflexus*, *Paradelphacodes paludosus* and *Oncodelphax pullulus*. The management of wet heaths presents many problems to conservation organisations as so many of the better sites are registered commons where stock grazing is difficult to arrange or regulate. Whereas the general principle of managing for habitat diversity and the retention of heath in its pioneer, building, mature and degenerate phases will be the over-riding priority, additional information on the particular micro-habitat features which are important for invertebrates will be an invaluable aid to management decisions.

Management is not such a problem on the dry, gravel heaths of Cardiganshire as the habitat structure is largely maintained as a result of the toxic metals in the deposits which form the substratum. The mine-spoil heaths are strongly influenced by the high toxicity of the lead and zinc ore which was discarded on the spoil-tips and the major threat to these sites comes from the desire to reclaim these 'barren wastes' and to level-out and grass-over the 'unsightly' heaps. Large colonies of graylings and mottled grasshoppers are present on these sites and glow worms *Lampyris noctiluca* have been reported from several of them, but otherwise their invertebrate interest is virtually unknown. It is pure speculation that these areas contain any significant invertebrate interest but in a Region with so few dry heath habitats it would be a pity to lose them to reclamation before their interest was known.

The shingle heaths of the river floodplains are also established on gravels with a high lead and zinc content and possibly owe their origin to the lead-mines upstream. These deposits were chiefly laid down about a hundred years ago but the heavy metals are only very slowly leaching from the soils. Occasional flooding probably also reduces the likelihood of scrub encroachment and a few sites are also lightly grazed. On current knowledge, river shingle heaths seem to be more or less restricted to northern Scotland and so the recent recognition of a small number of sites in Cardiganshire, ranging in size from a couple of hundred square metres to several hectares, is of great significance. There has been little opportunity so far for investigation of the fauna but already there are indications that there is great potential for exciting discoveries, with characteristic species of the southern English heaths, such as the carabids *Pterostichus lepidus* and *Amara equestris* and the handsome black and red bug *Alydus calcaratus*, having been recorded to date. Scores of *Nomada* solitary bees fly over the bands of bare silt which are such a major feature of some of these sites and surveys of the aculeate Hymenoptera could reveal a number of scarce and interesting species.

The heathlands of Dyfed are of recognised conservation importance for a variety of reasons and a high proportion of them are either owned and managed by conservation bodies (the National Trust and the Dyfed Wildlife Trust) or notified as Sites of Special Scientific Interest. Sites such as Dowrog Common and Brynberian Moor have been known for a long time as being of importance for their invertebrates but it is only in recent years that attention has been given to other, less well-known sites. There is sufficient information to show that the heaths of West Wales have a character all of their own, the southern elements being combined with species of the northern and western peatlands. This new impetus of invertebrate survey will be beneficial for the protection and conservation of heathlands in the Region but much will still remain to be learnt about the ecology of the heathland fauna.

Open water and its margins

Afon Tywi, Dyfed. [R.P. Bray]

The activities of the last Ice Age, which did so much to shape the landscape of the counties of Dyfed and Powys, gave rise to the network of valleys and depressions that forms the framework of the Region's freshwater resource today. Evidence of the Ice Age can be found in the high corries of the southern uplands, the meltwater channels of the major rivers, and the scattered kettle-hole basins of the boulder-clay deposits. In the last couple of hundred years the demands of industry and agriculture have led to the creation of new water-bodies as streams were dammed to provide water for the metal-mines, leats and canals were dug, huge areas of the uplands were flooded for hydro-electricity and drinking water purposes and, most recently, irrigation reservoirs flourished with the spread of potato-farming. There is undoubtedly more open water habitat available in the Region at present than at any time in the last thousand years and the current proliferation of ponds for conservation continues to add to this wealth.

Throughout the Region, rivers and streams dissect the countryside, most of which have an 'upland' character (i.e. stony-bottomed and fast-flowing with frequent erosive spates) although the lower reaches of some of the major rivers, such as the Tywi and the mid-Wye, meander slowly through fertile floodplains and are distinctively 'lowland' in nature. This distinction between river types is an important aid to an understanding of the range of invertebrates present in the watercourses of Dyfed and Powys as so many species are highly adapted to life within one regime or other. As with terrestrial habitats, micro-site complexity beneath the water's surface brings with it a host of species that are totally dependent upon the continuity of specific conditions. In upland rivers, the fauna is adapted to cope with the fast currents by clinging to stones or by sheltering within the river-bed gravels or bankside vegetation. Conversely, the sluggish flow of lowland river-sections reduces aeration of the water and only species which can tolerate the low oxygen levels of mid-summer (or can breathe air at the surface) are able to thrive. Water chemistry is an additional important factor in the distribution of river invertebrates and mineral-rich watercourses tend to support a more diverse fauna, with species such as the freshwater crayfish *Austropotamobius pallipes* which is only found in the richer streams and rivers in the east of the Region. The bryophyte-dominated upland rivers are chiefly of importance for their insect assemblages, with stoneflies, mayflies and caddisflies predominating. As nutrient levels increase, the non-insect invertebrates comprise a greater proportion of the species present, most noticeably the aquatic molluscs but also including freshwater worms, leeches, etc. Additional features which contribute to species-richness in flowing-water habitats include the presence of riffles and pools, the nature and extent of submerged and emergent vegetation, and the quality of adjacent river corridor habitats.

Several of the major rivers in the Region are recognised as being of national importance for conservation and outstanding in this regard are the River Wye and the Afon Teifi, both of which have been extensively sampled and found to contain unique assemblages of species amongst groups such as the caddisflies, stoneflies and mayflies. The Wye begins life as a trickling spring high on the slopes of Pumlumon and travels for some 250 km before joining the Severn estuary near Chepstow. The Upper Wye races across its stony bed but below Builth Wells velocity decreases and the river ambles through its broad floodplain. In the higher reaches, the spectacular golden-ringed dragonfly *Cordulegaster boltonii* patrols its territory on the acid streams whilst quieter, pebble-bottomed stretches are home for the aptly-named beautiful demoiselle *Calopteryx virgo*. With slower flows, as the river bottom changes from gravel to silt, the delicate banded demoiselle *C. splendens* replaces its close relative and regionally important colonies of the white-legged damselfly *Platycnemis pennipes* occur. Riffles in these middle reaches have produced most of the records of uncommon invertebrates, amongst which can be mentioned the caddisflies *Glossoma intermedia* and *Cheumatopsyche lepida*, the mayflies *Baetis digitatus* and *Potamanthus luteus*, the stonefly *Rhabdiopteryx acuminata*, and the riffle beetle *Stenelmis canaliculata*. The Wye, its tributaries, and several other streams in northern Powys are also important for their populations of freshwater crayfish. At present this is not an uncommon species nationally but it is under threat from a fungal disease which was introduced with the American signal crayfish *Pacifastacus leniusculus*. This disease, which is known as crayfish plague, endangers many populations of our native crayfish in England but as yet it does not appear to have reached mid-

Wales. In this context the Powys colonies take on an added significance as they may represent a safe stronghold for the freshwater crayfish as it is steadily eliminated from much of its range.

The Teifi is a peculiar river as its 'lowland' sluggish section is perched at 175 metres above sea level where the river seeps through the raised mires of Cors Caron. Below the great bogs, the river falls again with a gradient and flow characteristic of an upland-type river but it never manages to shake off the influence of the Cors Caron stretch and its aquatic vegetation contains an unusual mixture of upland and lowland species. This is also reflected in the distribution of the two demoiselles. *Calopteryx splendens* occurs abundantly along the river as it flows through the raised mires and is also common on stretches of reduced flow all the way down to Cardigan. *C. virgo*, on the other hand, is typically frequent along the upper river but can also be found all the way downstream to Cardigan and the two species often occur together in the lower reaches where their habitat requirements overlap. Extensive studies of the Teifi have shown that, despite its rather nutrient-poor waters, the macro-invertebrate fauna of the river is one of the richest in Britain. Maximum diversity is associated with habitats on the river's edge where features such as submerged tree-roots, emergent vegetation and moss-covered boulders provide shelter and food for the inhabitants. Nationally scarce species recorded so far include the mayflies *Baetis atrebatinus* and *B. digitatus*, the caddisflies *Ylodes simulans*, *Oecetis notata*, *Cheumatopsyche lepida* and *Chimarra marginata*, and the aquatic bug *Aphelocheirus aestivalis*.

Unlike many terrestrial habitats, most watercourses do not generally require positive management to maintain their importance for invertebrates and conservation effort is geared towards combatting the detrimental effects of Man's activities within the catchment. Changes in water quality due to acidification (which is linked to catchment afforestation), direct pollution through the input of toxic waste, slurry and silage liquor, or by eutrophication from the use of inorganic fertilisers on surrounding fields and the discharge of elevated levels of sewage, can seriously deplete the aquatic fauna. Similarly, channel-straightening schemes (which remove many of the important micro-site features of the river margin and alter the dynamics of the river current) and the regulation of rivers by the construction of dams (which reduce the sediment-bearing capacity of the river and hence alter the composition of the river-bed below the dam) can have major effects on the range of habitats available to invertebrates along a river's

length. The use of invertebrates to monitor river quality is universally accepted by the water authorities in Britain and the richness of the Wye and the Teifi reflects the fact that, by and large, they have so far escaped major deterioration by any of the above threats.

Although these two rivers are undoubtedly of prime importance for aquatic invertebrates, there are many other watercourses in the Region which are also of great significance. In northern Powys, the tributaries of the Afon Vyrnwy still maintain populations of the freshwater pearl mussel *Margaritifera margaritifera*, an inhabitant of acidic waters in northern and western Britain which has suffered a major decline in range as a result of pollution and over-collecting. This species, which is threatened throughout Europe and is legally protected in Britain, is extremely slow-growing. It does not reproduce until it is about twenty years old and may live for a century. Rivers such as the Dyfi, Severn, Rheidol, Ystwyth and Tywi support a good range of riffle beetles in their gravelly sections and the dytiscid *Deronectes latus* is probably widespread although nationally this is an uncommon inhabitant of western rivers. A speciality of the gravel-bed rivers is the tiny black-and-yellow *Bidessus minutissimus*, a water beetle that lives amongst fine gravel or sand in clean rivers. It has vanished from several of its former haunts in Britain as a result of pollution, river-engineering or changes in sediment deposition. The Severn, Wye, Teifi and Tywi support populations of the attractive club-tailed dragonfly *Gomphus vulgatissimus*, especially where the river is slow-flowing and there is bankside scrub or woodland to provide shelter for the maturing adults.

Ditches are another type of watercourse which, in some parts of Britain, can be important for freshwater invertebrates. Unfortunately, there do not seem to be any significant areas of grazing levels in the Region which contain good ditch systems and the best example is probably to be found on Ministry of Defence property at Pendine, but the fauna has not been sampled due to restrictions on access. The Leri dykes on the western edge of Cors Fochno do support a population of the variable damselfly *Coenagrion pulchellum* but they are probably too acidic for most of the soldier flies, snails, water beetles, etc. which are characteristic of the richer, mesotrophic and eutrophic ditches.

Canals are another kind of artificial watercourse and Powys has substantial lengths of the Montgomery and Brecon canals within its boundaries. An extensive survey of the former has shown that a number of scarce invertebrates are favoured by its sluggish flow and silt bottom along with its nationally important aquatic plant communities. The canals naturally lack the bank diversity of the lowland rivers they mimic but nonetheless, where they remain free of pollution and excessive disturbance, they provide sheltered stretches of slack water which are of regional value for invertebrate conservation. More than thirty species of freshwater molluscs have been recorded from the Montgomery Canal, including a number of species which are characteristic of calcium-rich waters such as *Bithynia leachii* and *Sphaerium rivicola* and others with a restricted distribution nationally such as *S. transversum*, *Pisidium moitessierianum* and *P. pulchellum*. The uncommon mayfly *Caenis robusta* and the water beetles *Haliplus heydeni*, *Noterus crassicornis* and *Ilybius guttiger* were also recorded during the

Club-tailed dragonfly *Gomphus vulgatissimus*. [A.P. Fowles]

survey and the white-legged damselfly is widely distributed.

The conservation of the aquatic environment cannot be divorced from the peripheral habitats that line the banks of our water-bodies as the ecology of so many of our freshwater invertebrates is dependent upon the maintenance of suitable conditions on the lake or river margin. Dragonflies, for instance, may live as nymphs for a year or two below the water's surface but many need emergent vegetation to climb up and complete the transformation into their short-lived adult state. Most species then require shelter away from the water's edge where the females can develop to sexual maturity without harrassment from the territorial males. Although some water beetles can pupate below the surface by tapping into the air-supply of aquatic plants, most water beetle larvae leave the water to find a suitable site for pupation as they make the change to air-breathing adults. Bankside foliage provides perches for aerial insects on which to rest and court or watch for prey and water plants are host to a suite of phytophagous species. Areas of bank that are free of vegetation are also valuable as there are many specialists amongst groups such as the beetles, spiders and flies that are restricted to this interface of damp, open ground. One of the most extreme habitats in this respect is the unstable banks of river shingle that pile up along the edges of the gravel-bed rivers. It is only recently that any attention has been paid to the highly-specialised community of invertebrates that inhabits such sites in Wales but it is already clear that several of the Region's rivers are of major importance for their shingle fauna.

Invertebrates living on shingle banks have to be able to endure the harsh conditions that are inherent in the creation of such features. During the winter spates the rivers erode their banks and the strong currents of the floodwater transport pebbles and boulders downstream until they are deposited in quieter stretches, often on the inside bend of meanders. Such spates create an annual upheaval on shingle banks that keeps them free of permanent vegetation and continually re-distributes the sands, gravels and larger stones that form the matrix of the habitat. Paradoxically, during low river-levels in the summer months, the surface layers of such banks suffer from drought as the water-table recedes and the inhabitants must find ways of coping with the arid conditions. The impressive wolf spider *Arctosa cinerea*, one of the biggest British spiders, overcomes these problems by constructing a burrow within deposits of fine gravel. Here it can maintain its humidity requirements by keeping in contact with the deeper layers of damp gravel. During the winter it retreats to the relative stability deep within the bank where it can remain submerged for long periods while the shingle above it is reshaped by the floods. Another spider, *Caviphantes saxetorum*, chooses to build its sheet web underneath a deeply-embedded boulder, its survival being dependent upon the floods being not strong enough to shift its home. Shingle beetles have two main strategies for winter survival; some are entirely fossorial (burrowing) and spend their lives amongst the tiny spaces between the gravel particles, whilst others leave the bank when the floods come and fly off to find shelter in scrub or rough grassland above the riverbank. River shingle which backs onto such terrestrial habitats will, therefore, be able to support a much more diverse fauna than sites which are bordered by improved pasture, for instance. Particle-size composition also determines the richness of the fauna and it appears that a matrix of sands and fine gravels, which have the capacity to retain moisture through capillary action, is important for a high proportion of the specialist inhabitants.

At present, few rivers in the region have been surveyed for their shingle invertebrate fauna but certainly the Severn, Wye, Rheidol, Ystwyth and Tywi have substantial areas of suitable floodplain. At Glasbury, on the Wye, the extensive banks of coarse sand and shingle fringed by wet woodland support a large number of nationally uncommon species including the rare click beetle *Negastrius sabulicola* and the empid fly *Tachydromia acklandi*. Shingle banks are important habitats for ground beetles and there are many species which are only found in such places — at Glasbury they include *Perileptus areolatus*, *Thalassophilus longicornis* and *Bembidion monticola*. A speciality of the Dyfed rivers is *Lionychus quadrillum*, a small ground beetle that had been considered extinct in Britain until its recent discovery in West Wales, where it appears to be widely distributed in the lowlands. Surveys of the Afon Ystwyth have revealed the presence of two other beetle species that had not been seen in Britain for many years. The five-spot ladybird *Coccinella 5-punctata* is now known to be fairly common on shingle banks in Dyfed where the adults feed on aphids living on riverside vegetation such as broom, thistles and knapweed. On the continent this is a common grassland beetle and the reasons behind its restricted distribution in Britain are unclear. The tiny rove beetle *Thinobius newberyi* is thought to be endemic to Britain and had only been known from a handful of specimens collected in Cumbria and the Spey Valley earlier this century. It has recently been discovered on the Ystwyth and

Rheidol in Cardiganshire where the adults live a subterranean existence within fine gravel deposits along the river's edge.

Some of the upland lakes in the region are also fringed by shingle on their wave-washed shores but as yet they have not been surveyed to determine whether or not they support a distinctive fauna like the gravel-bed rivers. These high-altitude lakes are generally poor in nutrients (oligotrophic) and their aquatic fauna is typically composed of only a few species which are tolerant of the acid waters. It could be expected that some of the corrie lakes of the Brecon Beacons, e.g. Llyn-y-fan Fawr, would contain members of the relict glacial fauna that is found in similar lakes in Snowdonia but there is no evidence of this as yet. The information that does exist suggests that the upland lake faunas are characteristically poor but very few have been adequately surveyed and their importance may be under-rated. Nonetheless, the marginal fens of such lakes, which are usually dominated by bog-mosses *Sphagnum* spp. and bottle-sedge, are inhabited by strong populations of dragonflies such as the black darter *Sympetrum danae*, the common hawker *Aeshna juncea*, and the keeled skimmer *Orthetrum coerulescens*, which is frequent on boggy ground around the inflows. At lower altitudes, the scarce reed beetle *Donacia obscura* has been found at Talley Lakes and Taliaris Lake and, as the species is associated with bottle-sedge growing in lake fen, it may prove to be quite widespread in the Region's uplands.

Although there are a few lakes in the lowlands which are oligotrophic, most of the water bodies there are richer in nutrients and this increases the diversity of the aquatic fauna. Food is more freely available as a result of the faster decomposition of organic matter and the presence of calcium salts in solution aids the development of shells and exoskeletons for invertebrate growth. This is particularly noticeable amongst the freshwater molluscs which are represented by many more species in mesotrophic waters than the handful of species that are capable of thriving in the upland lakes. Llangorse Lake in Breconshire, for instance, supported fifteen species of freshwater molluscs, including the large swan mussel *Anodonta cygnea* which is local in Wales, but problems with eutrophication (mainly from the inadequate treatment of sewage discharged into the lake) have probably reduced the diversity. Llangorse is the biggest lowland lake in South Wales and its shallow waters with gentle shelving sandy banks provided excellent habitats for a host of uncommon invertebrates, most notably the medicinal leech *Hirudo medicinalis*, but its value has been considerably affected by

nutrient enrichment and the disturbance from power-boats. Some of the problems have been overcome but it is doubtful whether conditions will ever be fully restored for its aquatic wildlife.

The richest body of standing water for invertebrates in the Region is probably the system of marl lakes at Bosherston in Pembrokeshire. Three narrow river valleys, which cut through the Carboniferous Limestone and emerge through the sand dunes at Stackpole Warren, were dammed between 150 and 200 years ago to produce 33 ha of shallow, lime-rich water. The calcium carbonate precipitates to form marl and there is vigorous growth of aquatic plants over much of the lake with large areas of lake bottom covered with the stonewort *Chara hispida*. The arms of the lake are reed-fringed and wooded, providing valuable micro-sites for species which live in the marginal habitats of aquatic systems. For instance, submerged tree-roots shelter the larvae of two nationally uncommon species of caddisfly, *Ecnomus tenellus* and *Orthotrichia costalis*, the latter at its only known Welsh site. Other noteworthy invertebrates at Bosherston include the ramshorn snail *Planorbis laevis*, the water boatman *Corixa affinis*, the water stick-insect *Ranatra linearis* and the caddis *Leptocerus tineiformis*. The only other comparable lake in the Region is the Witchett Pool on Laugharne Burrows. This is a 9 ha freshwater lake within the dune system at MoD Pendine which is known to contain a good dragonfly fauna, including the hairy dragonfly *Brachytron pratense*, but access restrictions have prevented further survey work.

Some of the larger lakes of the Region are occupied by the emperor dragonfly *Anax imperator* and the variable damselfly used to occur at Llangorse Lake (and perhaps still does). However, it is the smaller ponds which seem to be more important for dragonflies in mid and West Wales, with many sites holding nine or more species. Ponds which are not choked by vegetation are frequently inhabited by the broad-bodied chaser *Libellula depressa* and the scarce blue-tailed damselfly *Ischnura pumilio* is not uncommon in such sites. Both species tend to disappear as ponds mature and the dragonfly fauna is then dominated by the common darter *Sympetrum striolatum*, large red damsefly *Pyrrhosoma nymphula*, common blue damselfly *Enallagma cyathigerum* and emerald damselfly *Lestes sponsa*, along with several others.

As with flowing waters, the peripheral habitats of lakes and ponds are an important feature of their conservation value for invertebrates. Shallow water-bodies with fluctuating water-levels leave a band of bare mud during the dry summer months which is partially colonised by wetland plants. This fringe of moist ground is a valuable hunting-area for invertebrate predators, including ground beetles and shore bugs, and snails which are stranded as the water level drops fall prey to the larvae of sciomyzid flies. The Tywi ox-bows at Abergwili are a good example of this type of habitat, where the notable sciomyzids *Colobaea distincta* and *Pherbellia dorsata* have been recorded from the surrounding reed sweet-grass swamp, along with the local cranefly *Erioptera squalida*. Moderate levels of stock access can also produce similar saturated conditions on the margins of water-bodies and this can be a valuable form of conservation management, particularly if it is restricted to one section of the perimeter. Grazing and trampling on the southern bank ensures that the water is not shaded from the warmth of the sun whilst the opposite bank retains a fringe of vegetation for shelter and emergence sites. Marginal fens with stands of common reed or reedmace *Typha* spp.

are important for invertebrates from many different orders, including moths, hoverflies and spiders. The persistent dead stems and leaves also offer protection from the winter cold and rising water levels, whereas the vacated burrows of wainscot moth larvae and the clasping sheaths of *Typha* leaves often contain aggregations of over-wintering beetles and other invertebrates.

The status and distribution of invertebrate orders such as the dragonflies and caddisflies is relatively well-known in the Dyfed-Powys Region but for many other groups there is only patchy information available. The Region is well-endowed with a good range of water-bodies that are free from significant pollution or eutrophication and additional surveys are required to determine which sites are of conservation importance for invertebrates, particularly with regard to the upland lakes and river shingle communities. Beneath the water's surface thrives a diversity of invertebrates worthy of increased attention.

Lowland peatlands

Cors Caron, Dyfed. [I.J.L. Tillotson]

Peat develops in waterlogged conditions where the decomposition of dead plant material is slower than the rate at which it is laid down. This results in the build-up of organic matter and the development of characteristic plant communities which vary according to differences in the nutrient status of the peat. The input of nutrients is closely linked with the hydrology of the mire system (the way in which water reaches the surface layers of peat) as the lateral movement of water from adjacent habitats can introduce minerals which enrich the system. Peatlands are thus initially classified as either ombrotrophic (receiving their water supply from airborne moisture, i.e. rain, snow or mist) or minerotrophic (influenced by the flow of water across the ground). The high rainfall experienced over most of Wales ensures that Dyfed-Powys is well-endowed with peatlands of both types and the Region contains many excellent examples of a range of peatland communities. Ombrotrophic peat is commonest in the uplands where blanket mires clothe large areas of the rain-sodden land, but in the lowlands there are several nationally

important raised mires, such as Cors Caron, Cors Fochno and Rhosgoch. Minerotrophic peatlands (conventionally known as fens) occur widely in the lowlands and take the form of valley fens, basin fens, flush fens, etc. depending upon the topography in which they are situated. In 1978, the Nature Conservancy Council survey of Welsh Wetlands identified over 130 peatland sites above one hectare in Dyfed and Powys which were of conservation interest, with particular concentrations in Cardiganshire and Pembrokeshire. Although drainage is an ever-present threat to these wetlands, the rate of loss is relatively slow in the Region and the majority of these sites are still extant as, generally speaking, it is uneconomic to consider them for agricultural improvement. The invertebrate fauna of many of the Region's best peatlands has recently been surveyed by the Nature Conservancy Council in order to describe the communities associated with various peatland types and management practices. At present, only certain selected orders have been identified to species level and only a subjective analysis of community trends is available but, when the results are completed, lowland peatlands will undoubtedly be the best-known invertebrate habitats in the Region. This study builds upon the numerous casual observations, largely centred on the raised (ombrotrophic) mires, that have been recorded over the years.

Historically, most entomological recording has taken place on the two raised mire National Nature Reserves in Cardiganshire — Cors Caron and Cors Fochno. Intact raised mires are very rare in southern Britain and, although both of the Cardiganshire bogs have been modified to some extent in the past by peripheral drainage and peat-cutting, at 800 and 550 hectares respectively, they represent the finest examples of this type of peatland in England and Wales. Cors Caron actually consists of three separate bogs which have developed on the floodplain of the Afon Teifi and, besides the typical plant communities of the central domes, also has large areas of marginal fen (known as lagg) and willow carr. Entomological interest in the site is long-standing and Cors Caron has the distinction of being the southernmost locality in Britain for the large heath butterfly *Coenonympha tullia*. The diversity of wetland habitats in this peatland complex is reflected in the presence of sixteen species of dragonfly, including the keeled skimmer *Orthetrum coerulescens* on the fringes of the mire and the banded demoiselle *Calopteryx splendens* on the slow-flowing Teifi where it meanders past the three bogs. Until recent years, little was known of the less conspicuous elements of the fauna but this position is steadily being rectified. Moth-trapping, for instance, has revealed strong populations of several local mire specialists such as the grey scalloped bar *Dyscia fagaria* and the light knotgrass *Acronicta menyanthidis*, whilst the marsh oblique-barred *Hypenodes turfosalis* has also been recorded in recent years. Spiders, too, have been well surveyed and Cors Caron is one of only two sites in Wales for the attractive orb-weaver *Singa hamata* which builds its web in cross-leaved heath and other plants on the central domes. Results from the Welsh Peatland Invertebrate Survey have shown that a typical raised mire beetle fauna is present, including the uncommon carabid *Agonum ericeti* which seems to be more or less confined to ombrotrophic peat. Their sampling stations included an area on one of the domes which was severely burnt in August 1984 and it was striking that the ground beetles in this area included species such as *Bradycellus ruficollis* and *Notiophilus germinyi* which are more characteristic of heathland, whilst the expected fauna, such as *Pterostichus rhaeticus* and *Agonum ericeti*, was completely absent. Changes in

vegetation structure were also reflected in the abundance of the scarce cranefly *Limnophila glabricula* which appeared commonly in traps set on marginal fen which was cattle-grazed but was much scarcer in similar habitat nearby which was ungrazed.

Since 1986, the effect of burning on the invertebrate communities of raised mires has been investigated at Cors Fochno, where two-thirds of the dome were burnt in 1986. This fire was not as severe as the one on Cors Caron (where peat smouldered for several weeks) and occurred during a prolonged February frost. As a result, unlike Cors Caron, the fire raced across the mire surface and left the *Sphagnum* unaffected but it was severely damaged by subsequent frosts, completely changing the micro-climate for overwintering invertebrates. The evidence from the study to date indicates that this winter-burn has depleted the populations of most invertebrates on the burnt area of the mire but has not altered the species composition in such a dramatic way as the Cors Caron fire. It is anticipated that a slow recolonisation of the burnt mire will take place as the plant communities and vegetation structure are gradually restored to their normal balance. One species, however, has been seriously affected by the fire and its after-effects and, unfortunately, this is the most important insect species on Cors Fochno, the rosy marsh moth *Eugraphe subrosea*. After having been considered extinct in Britain for more than a hundred years, following the drainage of its known haunts on the Cambridgeshire fens, the rosy marsh moth was discovered on Cors Fochno in 1967. It feeds as a larva on bog myrtle and occasionally bog rosemary and used to occur in abundance all over the central dome on Cors Fochno (with estimates of larval density at one per four square metres). Although two other colonies have recently been discovered in northern Cardiganshire, this was definitely the species' stronghold in Britain. Observations on larval distribution showed that the rosy marsh moth completely disappeared from the burnt area of the mire and, despite the rapid recovery of its foodplants, did not begin to recolonise the damaged bog until 1990, five seasons after the fire. It is suspected that the reason why recolonisation took so long is linked to changes in vegetation structure. In particular, the absence of a litter-layer of dead cottongrass and purple moor-grass leaves deprived the larvae of a stable micro-climate in which to overwinter and they were unable to survive the frosts which penetrate into the mire's surface. One accidental fire, at a time of year when it is sometimes considered safe to burn peatland vegetation, seriously threatened

Rosy marsh moth *Eugraphe subrosea.* [*P. Waring*]

the major British population of rosy marsh moths and lessons must be learnt from this experience. Catastrophic events such as this, whilst perhaps benefitting the botanical interest of some peatlands, can destroy the subtle conditions that are necessary for the survival of invertebrates. Where necessary, burning (and other forms of radical management) must be carried out gradually in piecemeal fashion, to allow invertebrate populations time to recover.

Although the rosy marsh moth is Cors Fochno's most famous inhabitant there are, of course, many other species of interest to be found there. In common with Cors Caron, large heaths are abundant and, on sunny days, *Agonum ericeti* can be seen darting across the boardwalk which traverses the bog. Cors Fochno is of recognised international importance for its dragonfly fauna with the variable damselfly *Coenagrion pulchellum* on the peripheral dykes and species such as the hairy dragonfly *Brachytron pratense* and the small red damselfly *Ceriagrion tenellum* have benefitted from the creation of new water-bodies as fire-breaks in the old peat-cuttings. Bog bush crickets *Metrioptera brachyptera* occur here in one of their few Welsh sites and the short-winged conehead *Conocephalus dorsalis* is locally distributed around the bog fringes. So far, the other major raised mires of the Region have not received the same level of attention as Cors Caron and Cors Fochno but the Welsh Peatland Invertebrate Survey have investigated the picturesque valley mire of Esgyrn Bottom in Pembrokeshire and discovered the tiny money spider *Glyphesis servulus*. Previously this species was only known from three sites in Dorset and East Anglia but subsequently it has been found on several fens in South Wales. Rhosgoch, Radnorshire, is another raised valley mire with

considerable potential for the discovery of rare invertebrates. *Enochrus affinis*, *coarctatus* and *ochropterus*, which are scarce water beetles of acid mires, have been recorded here and the uncommon carabids *Blethisa multipunctata* and *Chlaenius nigricornis* are present on the seasonally-flooded marginal fen which is extensively developed at this site. In Carmarthenshire, the raised mire of Cors Goch Llanllwch is more or less unknown entomologically but it does support bog bush crickets and a colony of small red damselflies and can be expected to yield many other nationally uncommon species when it receives the attention it deserves.

Minerotrophic fens are widespread in the Region, where they are primarily associated with river valleys, glacial depressions and coastal levels. Some of the basin fens which have formed in pingos and kettleholes are rather acidic in character and consist of a floating mat of *Sphagnum* with abundant cottongrass, cranberry and round-leaved sundew. It had been anticipated that these relict habitats might contain a rich water beetle fauna comparable to the pingo systems of East Anglia but recent surveys suggest otherwise, probably as a result of the acidity of the Welsh fens. There is, however, one glacial relict species of invertebrate, the whorl snail *Vertigo lilljeborgi*, that occurs in one of the kettlehole fens of the Region. This snail seems to thrive best where there is a fluctuating water-table and hence is vulnerable to any attempts at regulation. Many of the pingo basin fens have had their ramparts breached and, where they have not been completely drained, the through-flow of water encourages a richer flora of bogbean, meadowsweet and marsh St John's wort. These flushed pingo fens are frequently inhabited by the hoverflies *Anasimyia lunulata* and *A. lineata* along with commoner species such as *Lejogaster metallina* and *Pyrophaena granditarsa*. Basin fens formed in hollows on mineral-rich soils support a lusher vegetation, often with stands of reedmace. A good example is found on the old turbary at Aberithon in Radnorshire where the hoverflies *Parhelophilus consimilis* and *Anasimyia contracta* breed in the reedmace stems. This site has had problems with its water-supply in the past but it is undoubtedly important for a range of wetland invertebrates which includes the scarce carabid *Elaphrus uliginosus*, the flightless water beetle *Agabus unguicularis* and the Red Data Book cranefly *Prionocera pubescens*. The raft spider *Dolomedes fimbriatus* also occurs here; this is a species which is far less common in Wales than in its English strongholds. Ox-bow fens alongside rivers such as the Wye and the Teifi are likely to have a similar fauna to the richer glacial basins but to date they have received few visits from entomologists and are worthy of further survey.

The many shallow valley fens of the Region show a similar gradation of trophic status to the basin fens. In Dyfed, where these habitats are best developed, the northern valleys of Cardiganshire tend to be relatively acidic whilst the southern fens of Carmarthenshire and Pembrokeshire are generally mesotrophic. Reedbeds are frequent on these shallow southern peats and dense stands of greater tussock sedge are a conspicuous feature. Phytophagous insects are generally abundant and include species of rather local distribution such as the leaf beetles *Phyllobrotica quadrimaculata* and *Chrysolina fastuosa* and the scathophagid fly *Norellisoma lituratum*. The slender groundhopper *Tetrix subulata* is not uncommon in areas with sparsely-vegetated zones of silty peat. Mats of decaying vegetation in these richer fens provide ideal habitat for many rove beetles which form a distinctive assemblage of species, including the handsome blue and orange *Paederus riparius*, *Tachinus signatus*, *Stenus latifrons*, *Philonthus quisquiliarius* and *Platystethus arenarius* amongst many others, and the local sylvanid beetle *Psammoecus bipunctatus*. Hoverflies of the genera *Anasimyia* and *Parhelophilus* are well represented in the valley fens whilst *Platycheirus fulviventris* and *P. scambus* are characteristic members of the fauna.

The samples gathered by the Welsh Peatland Invertebrate Survey are beginning to reveal some of the affinities of various groups on the fen peats. Soldier beetles of the genus *Cantharis* contain several good examples: *C. paludosa* and *C. figurata* are found chiefly on the more acidic fens whilst *C. pallida* appears to be restricted to the richest sites and *C. thoracica* is wide-ranging in tall fen habitats. Terrestrial molluscs are also responsive to differences in trophic levels. Acidic sites will support little more than the snail *Nesovitrea hammonis* and the ubiquitous black slug *Arion ater* but species-richness increases noticeably on the richer fens where *Arianta arbustorum*, *Ashfordia granulata* and *Succinea putris* are conspicuous members of the fauna. Members of the ground beetle genus *Agonum* are proving to be very useful as indicators of smaller-scale habitat differences, particularly as several species have poorly-developed powers of flight. This is well demonstrated on Llangloffan Fen, a rich valley fen on the banks of the Western Cleddau in Pembrokeshire which contains areas of grazed and ungrazed vegetation. Pitfall trapping in these areas of different management has shown that *Agonum thoreyi* is a characteristic inhabitant of fens with tall, dense vegetation where it often occurs with *A. fuliginosum*. Fens which are moderately grazed, such that there is an open structure containing scattered grass tussocks and a sparse litter-layer, support *A. moestum* and *A. viduum*. On permanently waterlogged ground *A. gracile*, tolerant of a wide range of fen types, is usually the dominant *Agonum* present.

Coastal fens which developed on flat ground as the sea level fell are a scarce resource in Dyfed, partly because most of the coastline is unsuited to such formations but also because this productive land has largely been reclaimed for agriculture. The best remaining examples are to be found in Pembrokeshire where Cors Penally, Goodwick Marsh and Castlemartin Corse are outstanding. The calcareous conditions favour soldier flies, such as *Oplodontha viridula*, and other Diptera which flourish in these base-rich sites include the craneflies *Limonia trivittata* and *Thaumastoptera calceata*, the scatophagids *Cordilura albipes* and *Spaziphora hydromyzina*, and the hoverflies *Chrysotoxum festivum* and *Tropidia scita*. Great green bush crickets *Tettigonia viridissima* and short-winged coneheads are also well-established on the coastal fens, although lesser marsh grasshoppers *Chorthippus albomarginatus*, which could be expected to occur, are seemingly absent from the Region.

The above account has been necessarily selective and has concentrated only on the major peatland types occurring in the lowlands of Dyfed-Powys. Peatland classifications subdivide these further but the evidence from invertebrate surveys suggest that there is considerable overlap in peatland faunas and sites with similar water-table and water-quality regimes will, broadly speaking, be capable of supporting similar faunas.

Thus, river fens, floodplain mires and valley fens, for example, will tend to support a similar range of species if they are generally comparable in terms of vegetation structure and management. The same is also true for the ombrotrophic mires and it is striking how similar are the various elements of the fauna of Cors Fochno (an estuarine raised mire) and Cors Caron (a floodplain raised mire at 160 metres above sea level). Differences arise where management, nutrient input and frequency of inundation exert changes on the vegetation which are reflected in the micro-habitats available to invertebrates. This is not to suggest that any single valley or basin fen can be taken as representative of all sites in the Region. Geographical position certainly has a part to play in shaping the fauna and past management (particularly the extraction of peat and the partial drainage of bogs) will also have brought about changes in species-composition. The wealth of peatland sites throughout the Dyfed-Powys Region provides an extensive refuge for a vast assemblage of species which are not uncommon at present but which are continually under threat from the drainage or deterioration of their required habitat. Analysis of the results from the Welsh Peatland Invertebrate Survey will give indications of the fauna associated with a range of conditions occurring on the peatlands but there is still a need for investigations into the important features of other components, willow and alder carr or aquatic habitats for instance, which have not been the subject of intensive survey.

Uplands

Mynydd Du, Powys. [R.P. Bray]

The upland environment dominates much of the landscape of the Dyfed-Powys Region but, despite this, it is a poorly-worked area for invertebrates and relatively little is known of the detailed distribution of species or how their populations have fared in the last fifty years or so as the character of the hills has changed. The major upland blocks of the Region are the Cambrian Mountains, forming the western backbone, and the southern ridge of the Brecon Beacons. The Cambrian Mountains, crowned by Pumlumon at 752 metres above sea level, are composed chiefly of Silurian and Ordovician mudstones, grits and shales giving rise to base-poor soils that support little in the way of plant diversity. The gentle slopes of many of the hills provide ideal conditions for the formation of blanket mire in this area of high rainfall (averaging *c.* 2500 mm per year on Pumlumon) and there are few crags and cliff-faces to break the undulating relief. In contrast, the Brecon Beacons (which reach 886 metres a.s.l. on Pen-y-fan) are geologically more diverse, consisting mainly of lime-rich Old Red Sandstone with a narrow band of Carboniferous

Limestone and acidic Millstone Grit. The effect of glaciation and weathering of the softer rocks has produced steep escarpments and botanically-rich cliff-ledges that escape the attentions of the sheep that swarm over most of the Brecon Beacons. Other upland blocks of importance in the Region include Mynydd Preseli in the south-west (highly-influenced by Pembrokeshire's mild Oceanic climate), Radnor Forest (an extensive blanket mire), Llanbrynmair Moor (blanket mire now largely afforested) and Berwyn (an extensive tract of sub-montane grassland and blanket mire). The predominant habitat of the unenclosed land above 300 metres a.s.l. is the acidic grassland of the upland sheepwalks, rough grazings that clothe vast areas with a cropped sward of mat-grass, sheep's-fescue and common bent. On wetter ground, particularly on the western hills, degraded blanket mire is dominated by tussocky purple moor-grass with patchy heather and cottongrass. The heather communities that are regarded as being so typical of the hill country are now restricted to scattered remnants where sheep are either stocked at low-density or are excluded altogether. Conifer plantations have most dramatically changed the upland landscape, particularly during an aggressive afforestation programme in the 1940s and 1950s but planting still continues today, even within designated Environmentally Sensitive Areas (ESAs).

Upland invertebrate faunas are typically composed of a limited number of species that are either totally montane in character or else are lowland species that are tolerant of the harsher environmental conditions. It is believed that many of the invertebrates which occur only on mountain tops have a relict distribution following the amelioration of the climate after the last glaciation and it is only at high altitudes that they can find conditions comparable to the tundra habitats that once covered the British Isles. However, for reasons which are not clearly understood, the uplands of Dyfed and Powys contain few of the montane species which are known from Snowdonia and amongst the beetles and spiders (the two groups which have been most thoroughly investigated at altitude in Wales) there are perhaps only fourteen species which fit this category. Pumlumon, perhaps because it is the northernmost high peak, has more montane species recorded than any of the other massifs in the Region and few characteristic upland species are currently known from the southern summits of the Brecon Beacons. The Pumlumon specialists are the money spiders *Lepthyphantes whymperi*, *Meioneta gulosa* and *Rhaebothorax morulus*; the dung beetle *Aphodius lapponum*; the rove beetles *Lesteva monticola*, *Arpedium brachypterum* and *Geodromicus longipes*; and the ground beetles *Pterostichus adstrictus* and *Patrobus assimilis*. It is doubtful if any of these are restricted to Pumlumon, however, and several are already known from many other sites in the Region. Other montane species recorded on upland blocks elsewhere in Dyfed-Powys are the spider *Porrhomma montanum* from the watershed mire of Figyn Blaen-brefi, the weevil *Otiorhynchus nodosus* recorded from the Brecon Beacons, the widespread ground beetles *Nebria gyllenhali* and *Pterostichus aethiops*, and the rove beetle *Quedius boopoides* which is known from several of the Region's blanket mires. None of these species occur in any abundance on the mountain tops (with the occasional exception of *A. lapponum* which feeds on sheep dung) and the commonest invertebrates encountered are usually hardy lowland species that can tolerate the exposure and high rainfall. Amongst the spiders, for instance, *Coelotes atropos* and *Robertus lividus* are widely distributed in the lowlands and also occur commonly under stones on the summit grasslands. Similarly, the ground beetles *Carabus*

arvensis and *C. problematicus* are dominant members of the upland carabid fauna but both occur in lowland habitats, particularly heathlands, as well.

Moving down from the higher summits to the sub-montane habitats lying between 300 and 600 metres, the less exposed grasslands, moorlands and mires support a greater diversity of species. The small number of butterflies which occur regularly in the hills are to be found at these altitudes, particularly where sheep grazing is not too excessive. A scarce inhabitant of a few blanket mires in northern Powys is the large heath *Coenonympha tullia*, which feeds on hare's-tail cottongrass as a larva. More frequent inhabitants are the small heath *C. pamphilus* (the only widespread butterfly of the uplands) and the green hairstreak *Callophrys rubi*, which occasionally swarms over bilberry moors in early summer. Sheltered valleys may contain peacocks *Inachis io*, ringlets *Aphantopus hyperantus* or meadow browns *Maniola jurtina* but the only other widely distributed butterfly of the upland moors is the small pearl-bordered fritillary *Boloria selene*, colonies of which occur locally in wet hollows with plenty of marsh violets, the larval foodplant. Day-flying moths are also conspicuous at these middle-altitudes, particularly the heather-feeders such as common heath *Ematurga atomaria* and emperor *Saturnia pavonia*. Geometrid moths frequently flushed from cover during the day include the northern spinach *Eulithis populata*, striped twin-spot carpet *Coenotephria salicata* and grey mountain carpet *Entephria caesiata*, whilst common noctuids of the uplands include antler moth *Cerapteryx graminis*, true lover's knot *Lycophotia porphyrea* and Haworth's minor *Celaena haworthii*. The uplands of Dyfed-Powys are not particularly noted for their moth fauna (although this is a rarely-worked habitat by lepidopterists in the Region and there may be many exciting discoveries to be made) but some nationally uncommon species, such as the glaucous shears *Papestra biren*, scarce silver Y *Autographa interrogationis*, smoky wave *Scopula ternata* and golden-rod brindle *Lithomoia solidaginis*, are widely distributed in the Region. Larvae of the Ashworth's rustic *Xestia ashworthii* have been found on cliff-ledges of the northern outliers of Pumlumon and there are old records for the red carpet *Xanthorhoe munitata*. Both of these species are regarded as true upland moths and the former is endemic to the mountains of northern Wales.

Dragonflies, too, can be found in suitable habitats in the hills, with peaty pools in the blanket mires containing black darters *Sympetrum danae*, common hawkers *Aeshna juncea*, four-spotted chasers *Libellula quadrimaculata* and common blue damselflies *Enallagma cyathigerum*. More local is the keeled skimmer *Orthetrum coerulescens* which can occasionally be seen hunting over flushed areas at the outflow of lakes and on seepages on the lower slopes. The milder Oceanic conditions of Mynydd Preseli in Pembrokeshire permit the rare southern damselfly *Coenagrion mercuriale* to reach 300 metres a.s.l., the highest site in Britain for this 'Mediterranean' species which is more usually associated with lowland wet heaths.

A common beetle of the upland mires is the metallic, variably-coloured, reed beetle *Plateumaris discolor* which develops on the roots of cottongrass. Although this species also occurs on lowland peatlands, it is most frequently encountered on blanket mire throughout the Region. Other common beetles of the heather-dominated communities include the click beetle *Ctenicera cuprea* and the small weevil *Micrelus ericae* which mines the stems of heather. The large and attractive rove beetle *Staphylinus erythropterus* is regularly present on upland peat but the commonest staphylinid found in such habitats is probably *Olophrum piceum*. On open sheepwalks, the curious pill beetle *Byrrhus pilula* is abundant but easily overlooked as it convincingly resembles a ball of sheep dung when it retracts its legs beneath its body. Presumably it does not fool the lumbering adult dor beetles *Geotrupes stercorosus* as they roam the high grasslands in search of dung! A typical acidic peatland assemblage of ground beetles occurs on the blanket mires in which *Pterostichus diligens*, *P. rhaeticus* and *Agonum fuliginosum* are the most abundant, along with the tiny *Dyschirius globosus* which burrows into bare peat

on eroded areas of the watersheds. *Agonum ericeti* is not uncommon on the deeper peats of the ombrotrophic (rain-fed) mires, whilst drier heather moors are inhabited by carabids such as *Bradycellus ruficollis* and *Olisthopus rotundatus* which hunt their prey of springtails and mites amongst the leaf-litter beneath the heather clumps. A recent unexpected discovery in the Powys uplands is the nationally rare *Trechus rivularis*, small numbers of which were found on one of the few remnants of unafforested blanket mire left on Llanbrynmair Moors. This Red Data Book carabid was previously known from just four lowland fens in eastern England and was only regularly found at Wicken Fen in Cambridgeshire.

There is little documented information available for most other invertebrate groups in the uplands of Dyfed-Powys. Present knowledge indicates, as expected, that the fauna contains a high proportion of species with a northern and western distribution in Britain and this is demonstrated by initial results from the limited sampling of Diptera that has been undertaken so far. In the family Muscidae, several nationally uncommon species, such as *Coenosia trilineella*, *C. paludis* and *C. perpusilla*, which are chiefly known from Scotland and northern England, have been found on some of the Cardiganshire watershed mires. Another rarity, the caddisfly *Oxyethira mirabilis*, has just been discovered on a handful of upland sites in Dyfed where the larvae inhabit shallow runnels flowing through areas of bare or partially-vegetated peat. This species was last seen in Britain, prior to this discovery, in 1904 at its only known site on Rannoch Moor in Scotland.

The vastness of upland habitats throughout

Pill beetle *Byrrhus pilula* [R.S. Key]

***Hydrophilus piceus* (Coleoptera):** Restricted to the ditch systems of a few grazing levels in southern Britain, the great silver water beetle is not uncommon in the reens of the Gwent Levels.
(Photograph by R.S. Key.)

Redwick, Gwent Levels: Cattle grazing is an important feature of ditch systems as trampling creates permanently moist muddy shelves along the ditch bank. The wet soils of the 'poached' margins are ideal for species with semi-aquatic larvae, including many craneflies and other wetland Diptera.
(Photograph by A.P. Fowles.)

***Chalcis sispes* (Hymenoptera):** The status of most parasitic wasps in Britain is poorly known but this distinctive species is genuinely rare. It parasitises the aquatic larvae of soldier flies that inhabit the ditch systems of coastal grazing levels.
(Photograph by R.S. Key.)

River Dee, Clwyd: Tree-lined banks are an important feature of rivers as the tree roots provide underwater shelter for a range of aquatic invertebrates. The Dee is the best of the major lowland rivers in North Wales with long stretches having suffered little from bankside modification. (Photograph by A.P. Fowles.)

Arctosa cinerea **(Araneae):** This wolf spider is one of the largest spiders in Britain. It is found only on the gravel banks of rivers in the north and west of the country, inhabiting burrows underneath large pebbles. (Photograph by M.E.N. Majerus.)

Coccinella quinquepunctata **(Coleoptera):** The five-spot ladybird is unusual in that it is widespread in a variety of habitats in mainland Europe but in Britain it is confined to sparsely-vegetated river shingle. Several of the larger rivers in southern Wales support populations of this interesting beetle. (Photograph by M.E.N. Majerus.)

Afon Rheidol, Dyfed: The gravel-bed rivers of Wales form innumerable shingle banks where the floodplain is not constrained. These superficially lifeless collections of pebbles are the home of a specialised group of invertebrates that can tolerate regular flooding and frequent upheaval of the substrate by flash floods. River shingle is a neglected habitat but one which supports many rare invertebrates for which Welsh rivers are a major stronghold. (Photograph by A.P. Fowles.)

Britain precludes the detailed investigation of the distribution of invertebrates and conservation of the more specialised elements of the fauna is reliant upon an understanding of the environmental factors which favour the scarcer species. Large expanses of the uplands are subject to one form of designated protection or another, as National Parks, Sites of Special Scientific Interest, National Trust property, Common Land, Environmentally Sensitive Areas, etc., but afforestation and agricultural improvement still take their toll of significant areas of value to upland wildlife. More insidious is the ever-increasing density of sheep in the hills, gradually eroding blanket peat and diminishing the structural diversity of the vegetation. Few of the protected areas have controls to halt, let alone reverse, this increase. There is a tendency to believe that, because of the apparent uniformity of the Dyfed-Powys uplands and the huge area they cover, suitable habitats of value to invertebrate conservation are bound to survive whatever the pressures on the land. Further survey work, and particularly ecological studies, are required to determine how justified we are to hold this belief.

A habitat which is upland in location in Dyfed-Powys, but not in character, is the cave environment. Beneath the Carboniferous Limestone to the south of the Brecon Beacons lies Ogof Ffynnon Ddu, one of the largest cave systems in Britain and biologically the best-known. The cave invertebrate fauna has been the subject of considerable research and survey at this site, with emphasis placed on determining the inter-relationships between species and their micro-habitat preferences. Although, on present evidence, the British cave fauna is rather poor in terms of species-richness in comparison with continental Europe, nonetheless there are a number of interesting species which are confined to these subterranean habitats. It appears that the major sources of food for the specialised inhabitants are organic material which is brought into the cave along the underground waterways or as spores released from the microscopic fungi which thrive on the dank environment. At the bottom of the food-chain are the mites and springtails living on the surface film of cave pools or on algal films which coat the walls of the cave passages. Many of the cave inhabitants are also found above ground in suitable dark and humid locations but at least two of the species of springtails in Ogof Ffynnon Ddu, *Onychiurus schoetti* and *Pseudosinella dobati*, are entirely troglobitic (confined to subterranean habitats). They, in turn, are preyed upon by the cave shrimp *Niphargus fontanus* which lives in quiet pools away from the main flow of the underground streams. Another troglodyte, the cave waterlouse *Proasellus cavaticus*, is also poorly-adapted to cope with water-currents and inhabits thin films on rock faces where it probably grazes on algae. Two other aquatic crustaceans found in Ogof Ffynnon Ddu, the amphipod *Crangonyx subterraneus* and the ostracod *Cypridopsis subterranea*, are presently known from few other sites in Britain. However, for obvious reasons, few cave systems have been adequately sampled, and we are a long way from being able to evaluate the conservation importance of any single system for its invertebrates.

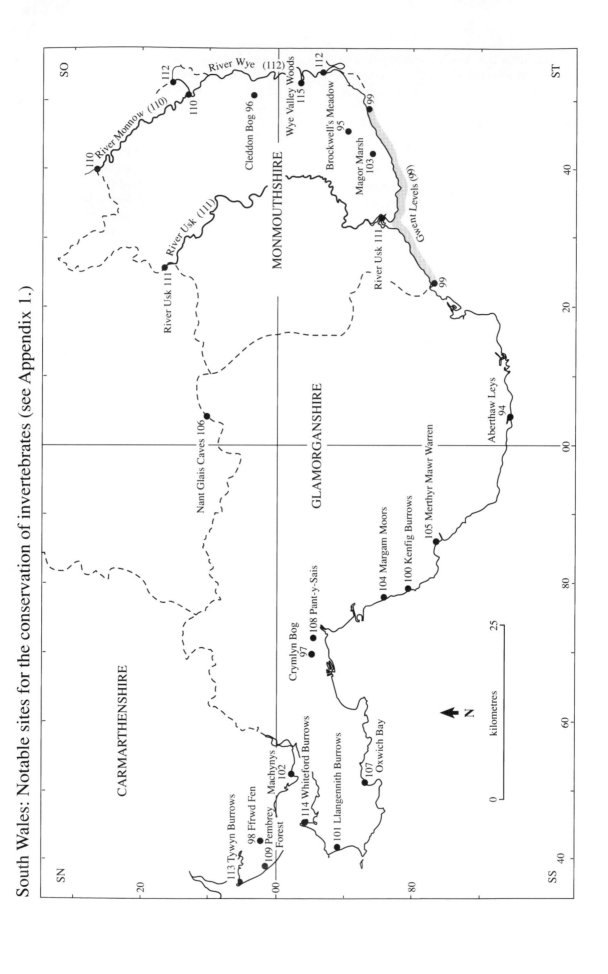

South Wales: Notable sites for the conservation of invertebrates (see Appendix 1.)

South Wales

Nicholaston, West Glamorgan. [A.P. Fowles]

Introduction

The Region of South Wales considered by this Review corresponds to the area administered by the Nature Conservancy Council's Regional Office in Cardiff prior to reorganisation in April 1991. This comprises the modern counties of Gwent, South Glamorgan, Mid Glamorgan, West Glamorgan and the Llanelli Borough of Dyfed. Following the formation of the Countryside Council for Wales there has been a change in the Region's boundaries, shedding Llanelli Borough and gaining the Brecon Beacons National Park. As this overview is based on information collated for the old Region, the discussion of sites and species of particular significance for invertebrate conservation in South Wales refers to the former, pre-1991, boundaries. For the purposes of biological recording this corresponds to the Watsonian vice-counties of Monmouthshire and

Glamorganshire, with part of Carmarthenshire (Llanelli Borough) and a small area of Breconshire which was incorporated into Gwent and Mid Glamorgan under the 1974 boundary revision. It is the most densely-populated part of Wales, including within its boundaries the major centres of Swansea, Cardiff, Newport, Llanelli, etc., and this has a major bearing on the legacy of semi-natural habitats and their conservation in the future. Despite the urban sprawls of the coastal cities and the mining towns of the northern valleys it is a region of contrasts. Traditional farming on the Gower peninsula and the pastoral economy of the fertile lands of east Gwent are worlds away from the crowded industry of steelworks and coal mines but there are important wildlife sites in each. Much of Mid Glamorgan is high ground dissected by valleys running down from the Brecon Beacons, the intervening plateaux bearing huge conifer plantations or the scars of coal-mining. Remote sheep-grazings do survive on these uplands though and agriculture is the major land use in most districts of the Region.

The solid geology of South Wales is dominated by the great coalfield basin which occupies most of Mid and West Glamorgan and Llanelli Borough. Throughout the Region the rocks are mainly of sedimentary origin with only a few minor examples of igneous intrusion in the extreme east and west. The surface outcrop of the coalfield is composed largely of sandstones, with shales, of the Silesian Pennant Measures encircled by the Coal Measures and Carboniferous Limestone. The western tip of the Gower peninsula is formed of Lower Devonian Sandstones and much of eastern Gwent lies on Old Red Sandstone. Another band of Carboniferous Limestone is cut through by the Wye Valley above Chepstow and runs parallel to the coast towards Cardiff. The southern part of the Region is a mixture of limestone outcrops and mudstones and shales of the Lower Lias and Triassic. This is an area of fertile soils which occupies much of the district known as the Vale of Glamorgan. The geomorphological features of the Region have been shaped by a complex glacial history in which ice-sheets from the Brecon Beacons and sea-ice moving up the Bristol Channel have left their mark on the landscape. The numerous U-shaped valleys and the corries in the northern scarp of the Pennant sandstone are evidence of these events. Surface deposits mask much of the country rock and come in a variety of forms: marine alluvium on the Gwent Levels, boulder clay overlying the coalfield basin, and widespread periglacial deposits of sand and gravel. Subsequent weathering and reworking of these deposits gives rise to 'head', an important feature for nature conservation on the cliffs of Gower. Considerable periodic changes in sea level have also left their mark on the South Wales landscape and, in more recent times, severe sand storms in the thirteenth and fourteenth century were probably responsible for initiating the formation of the Region's dune systems. Hill peat is not as widespread as it is in much of Wales but areas such as Blorenge in Gwent do have substantial blanket bogs.

It can be seen from this very generalised account of the geological and geomorphological features of the Region that there is a variety of substrates and a diverse topography on which the mantle of wildlife habitats occurs. Some of these are undoubtedly of national importance for nature conservation in general and invertebrate

conservation in particular. Two different types of habitat formation on the coast are of prime significance — the major dune systems and the ditch systems of the Gwent Levels. The extent and variety of the duneland sites is remarkable and it is invidious to select the best examples to represent this excellent series. However, the current level of recording suggests that Tywyn Burrows in Llanelli Borough and Kenfig Burrows and Merthyr Mawr Warren in Mid Glamorgan probably contain the fullest range of scarce and typical sand dune invertebrates. There are several other top-class sites, such as Oxwich and Whiteford Burrows on the Gower. Together they represent a stronghold for many restricted invertebrates, including the beetles *Dichronychus equiseti*, *Nebria complanata*, *Tychius quinquepunctatus* and *Glocianus pilosellus*, the flies *Thereva fulva* and *Pamponerus germanicus*, and many species of bees and wasps. The Gwent Levels are practically unique in Wales and are amongst the top five grazing marshes in Britain with regard to their ditch fauna. This vast area of reclaimed wetland has some 1400 kilometres of open ditches and provides a valuable refuge for aquatic and semi-aquatic invertebrates. Perhaps of greatest importance are the strong populations of the rare soldier fly *Odontomyia ornata* and the great silver water beetle *Hydrophilus piceus*.

Peatlands are not generally well-represented in the Region but the rich tall fens of the coastal zone are exceptional. This is a habitat type which is not widespread in Wales and the faunas show more affinity with the tall fens of southern and eastern England. The complex of habitats on the edge of Swansea at Crymlyn Bog and Pant-y-Sais support a vast number of rare species, some of which, such as the soldier beetle *Silis ruficollis* and the jumping spider *Marpissa radiata*, are more typical of the East Anglian fens. As with the dune systems, there are many fine examples of tall fens in the Region — Magor Marsh in Gwent and Ffrwd Farm in Llanelli Borough, for instance — and their conservation is an important priority.

South Wales has few natural lakes but its numerous ponds are a haven for dragonflies and uncommon species, such as the hairy dragonfly *Brachytron pratense*, the ruddy darter *Sympetrum sanguineum* and the black-tailed skimmer *Orthetrum cancellatum*, are reasonably widespread. Many of Glamorgan's rivers and streams have suffered a history of pollution and modification but within Gwent's boundaries there are three fine rivers, the Monnow, the Usk and the Wye. The fauna of the lower Wye is not as well known as its middle and upper reaches in Dyfed-Powys, but the Monnow supports an outstanding fauna, both in the river channel and on its banks. The riffle beetle *Normandia nitens* is confined to the Monnow and a few other rivers on the Wye catchment and the mayfly *Potamanthus luteus* is another national rarity present here. The assemblage of craneflies on the sandy banks of the Monnow is probably without parallel in England and Wales (although the Usk is also important for this family of insects) and the beetles of undisturbed sandy banks are also of great interest, including the click beetle *Negastrius sabulicola* and many ground beetles and rove beetles.

The remaining habitat formations in the Region are too poorly worked to allow an adequate assessment of their value for invertebrate conservation as a whole. On present evidence it appears that upland habitats are of limited significance, although the only British population of the Silurian moth *Eriopygodes imbecilla* occurs on the Gwent moorlands. Lowland heathlands are practically confined to the Gower Commons, where frequent burning reduces their interest for invertebrates. These commons are a mixture of unimproved grassland, mires and heath and cover a considerable proportion of the peninsula. Such an extent of semi-natural habitat cannot be entirely without interest and many of the commons support colonies of marsh fritillaries *Eurodryas aurinia*. It is very likely that the invertebrate interest is much greater than current knowledge indicates and detailed surveys would be rewarding. The pastures of the South Wales Coalfield, particularly in West Glamorgan, also contain marsh fritillary colonies but otherwise there is very little invertebrate information available. Woodlands are similarly unexplored in modern times, though in the past sites such as the Oxwich Woods, Cwrt-yr-ala, Castell Coch, and the Clyne woodlands yielded many rare species to the Glamorgan entomologists. The lime woods of the Wye Valley are home to the very rare scarce hook-tip moth *Sabra harpagula* and this area is well known to lepidopterists, but in general there needs to be a much greater degree of entomological recording in the Region's woodlands.

Historically, Glamorgan was well-served by amateur invertebrate zoologists, such as L.W. Dillwyn who, in 1829, produced a pioneering account of beetles in the Swansea district; and the County History, published in 1936, contains impressive faunal lists that, for most orders, are still without comparison in the rest of Wales. It is a reflection of the level of interest in entomology in the area that a Penarth Entomological Society was formed in 1888 and although this only lasted for about ten years it was until recently the only such society to be formed in Wales. For fifty years or so, this role was taken over by the Cardiff Naturalists' Society, who published many significant papers on the local invertebrates in their *Transactions*.

The decline in recording seems to have occurred in the 1950s and it would appear that the number of resident entomologists dwindled considerably. There were still a number of individuals who published occasional notes on the South Wales fauna and some, such as E.A. Fonseca, who diligently recorded particular groups for a considerable number of years. The South Wales coast was a favoured locality for many visiting entomologists from southern England but curiously there seems to have been a decline in their activities as travel became easier. At least there seems to be comparatively little published information in the 1950s and 1960s. In the mid-seventies a revival began which has continued slowly to the present. This coincided with a national upsurge of interest in the Lepidoptera and Odonata and the range of groups covered continues to expand.

Gwent almost certainly shares a similar history of recording to Glamorgan but very little has been collated on the county's fauna and details of the level of entomological survey in the past are scant. The Wye Valley has certainly attracted lepidopterists to its gorge woodlands for a long time. Elsewhere in the county there must have been few resident entomologists, a situation which continues to this day. Much the same can be said of Llanelli Borough, dependent for so long on the efforts of a handful of individuals, such as Arthur Price of Kidweli. T.W. Barker published early lists of Carmarthenshire's Lepidoptera and Odonata but other groups were largely neglected.

There has, of course, always been the University Colleges of Cardiff and Swansea and the National Museum of Wales at Cardiff to represent the professional and academic side of invertebrate taxonomy and ecology. These organisations have carried out significant studies on a number of specialised topics, although greater involvement by these bodies would be a boon in encouraging invertebrate recording and conservation locally. The emphasis within the Region has now swung more towards a broadening of the skills of the general naturalist and invertebrate concerns play a much greater role in the activities of the local Wildlife Trusts and the Naturalists' Societies. There are local groups covering dragonfly surveys and butterfly conservation and a wider treatment of the subject of invertebrate conservation is afforded by the Dyfed Invertebrate Group and, in the near future, a South Wales Invertebrate Group. The Nature Conservancy Council has contributed on the survey side with studies of the Gwent Levels and South Wales peatlands and many of the National Nature Reserves are important sites where management for invertebrates is a major concern. As the need to cater for invertebrates in the conservation of our natural heritage is increasingly understood, it is most welcome that there is this growing trend to harness the skills and knowledge of conservationists and invertebrate zoologists. South Wales has a great deal to offer invertebrate conservation nationally and this trend must be encouraged and sustained if the Region's fauna is to prosper in the future.

Coastlands

Pembrey Burrows, Dyfed. [J.B. Ratcliffe]

Coastal habitats dominate any account of the natural history of South Wales Region and this is equally true in terms of invertebrate conservation. The extent and quality of the sand dune systems in particular are probably only matched elsewhere in Britain by the North Norfolk Coast, and sites such as Merthyr Mawr, Whiteford Burrows and Tywyn Burrows are undeniably of national importance for the conservation of the invertebrate faunas of sand dunes and their associated habitats. The entomological richness of the South Wales belt of sand dunes is well known and there is a long tradition of recording which extends back into the last century when few other areas of Wales received any attention from entomologists. This has been a classic case of 'honeypot' recording and the appeal of the dune faunas has been to the detriment of other habitat types, an imbalance that is perhaps more true today than in previous decades. Nonetheless, the South Wales dunes deserve recognition for the richness of their faunas and the quality of the habitat features which sustain them. They are very much

the 'jewel in the crown' of the Region's contribution to invertebrate conservation and they are a credit to all those conservationists and local authorities who have worked hard together to ensure their protection. Their survival in the face of pressures from industry, tourism and urbanisation is remarkable and, whilst there have been unfortunate losses in the past, it would appear that the existing dune systems are free from all but the threat of encroaching sea buckthorn thickets.

The importance of these dunes lies chiefly in their extent as the larger complexes contain within them a more complete range of habitat features in the dune succession, contributing to the overall diversity of the invertebrate fauna. It is often the inland, stabilised sections which are the first to be lost to agricultural improvement or industrial development and the rich faunas of mature dune grassland are therefore only fully represented in sites that have retained most of their integrity, such as Merthyr Mawr or Tywyn Burrows. On these calcareous sands the dune grassland is spectacularly floriferous and it is no surprise that many of the South Wales dunes are renowned for their assemblages of bees and wasps. The compacted sand of the mature dunes is ideal for burrowing and the abundance of nectar sources ensures a good food supply for bees whilst plant diversity contributes to a wealth of invertebrate prey for the sand dune wasps. Merthyr Mawr is particularly ideal for aculeate Hymenoptera as the dunes overlie ridges of Carboniferous Limestone, creating sheltered gulleys with varied aspects for breeding. A speciality of these dunes is the cuckoo bee *Coelioxys mandibularis* and other rarities include *Colletes marginatus* and *Oxybelus mandibularis*. The dune grassland at Tywyn Burrows is the haunt of large populations of marbled whites *Melanargia galathea*, marsh fritillaries *Eurodryas aurinia* and small blues *Cupido minimus*. Damper areas here support the scarce hoverfly *Microdon mutabilis*, which develops as a larva inside ants' nests.

Many of the South Wales dune systems have extensive slacks, a feature which is better developed in Wales and the southwest of England than elsewhere in Britain and which is a strong point of the Region. Dune slacks differ in character in terms of their age, the proximity of the summer water-table, the duration of seasonal flooding, the calcium content of the sand deposits, the degree of rabbit grazing, etc. Each type of slack contains its own distinctive faunistic elements and there is great variety and richness in this aspect of the Region's dunes. Slacks dominated by creeping willow, as at Whiteford Burrows for instance, are frequently bejewelled by the bright red leaf beetle *Chrysomela populi* while the flowers are visited by the mining bee *Colletes cunicularius* and the hoverfly *Eumerus sabulonum*. Hemiptera are represented by the local species *Globiceps cruciatus*, *Monosynamma sabulicola* and *Macropsis impura*. Open, wetter slacks can have important assemblages of wetland flies, such as *Dolichopus notatus* and *Hercostomus nigriplantis*. Around the mossy margins of several of the slacks on Tywyn Burrows Cepero's groundhopper *Tetrix ceperoi* reaches the northern limit of its British range. Also on Tywyn, slightly brackish, fenny slacks are the only existing British locality for the black and orange ground beetle *Panageus crux-major*. This species used to be widely distributed in fens and marshes in southern England and Wales but has apparently disappeared from all apart from Tywyn Burrows and the maintenance of this presently healthy population is a conservation priority. The margins of these slacks have narrow belts of sea club-rush which shelter huge numbers of the short-winged conehead *Conocephalus dorsalis* and the weevil *Notaris bimaculatus* is another distinguished inhabitant.

The unstable habitats of the shifting sands amongst the fore dunes and embryo dunes demand specialised adaptations of their inhabitants to survive the arid, exposed conditions. As a result the fauna tends to be limited in terms of species numbers but contains a high proportion of invertebrates that are entirely restricted to areas of mobile sand. High tourist pressure can severely deplete the fauna but in relatively undisturbed areas there thrives a distinctive suite of species. Although there is geographical variation in the components of this assemblage around the coasts of Britain, neighbouring dune systems tend to have more or less identical faunas in the fore dune zone. The South Wales group of dunes is notable for its predators. Together with the dunes of West Wales they constitute the British headquarters for the robber fly *Pamponerus germanicus* and the stiletto fly *Dialinura anilis*. Other nationally scarce species include the tiger beetle *Cicindela maritima*, the ant-mimicking spider *Synageles venator*, and the carrion-feeding beetle *Hypocaccus rugiceps*. Undisturbed strandlines are also of conservation value for their characteristic invertebrates and the tangles of driftwood and seaweed can shelter a vast abundance of rove beetles, kelp flies, etc. in addition to the ubiquitous sandhoppers. Several of the Region's dunes have large populations of the uncommon woodlouse *Armadillidium album*, which is entirely restricted to sandy strandlines, whilst the speciality of the shores of the Bristol Channel is the handsome cream and yellow ground beetle *Nebria complanata*. This gregarious species shelters under driftwood during the day and emerges to prey chiefly on sandhoppers at night. Attempts to 'tidy-up' beaches can be highly detrimental to *Nebria* and as most of its British colonies are located in Glamorganshire and Carmarthenshire there is an onus on conservationists in the Region to ensure that strandline disturbance is kept to a minimum. Beach barbecues also pose a serious threat.

Away from the dune systems information on the composition of the non-marine invertebrate faunas of coastal habitats in South Wales is very patchy. This is unfortunate, for whilst it is clear that the dunes are of national importance there is also a good range of other habitat types which are of sufficient quality to indicate that they too are likely to be of great value for invertebrate conservation. The Burry Inlet, for example, contains the second largest area of saltmarsh in Britain (most of which is of great value for wildlife conservation) yet the terrestrial invertebrate fauna is practically unknown. These marshes are extremely varied in structure and botanical composition and many contain extensive creek systems which offer important

Ground beetle *Nebria complanata*.
[R.S. Key]

conditions for burrowing invertebrates in the free-draining, aerated sediments of the creek walls. One of the best-worked areas is the floristically-diverse saltmarsh at the Leys, Aberthaw. Surveys here have revealed that a suite of nationally uncommon phytophagous beetles is associated with the stands of sea beet, sea plantain, etc., including the weevils *Polydrusus pulchellus* and *Mecinus collaris* and the leaf beetles *Chaetocnema sahlbergi* and *Longitarsus plantago-maritimus*. Scattered records from other marshes in the Burry Inlet, or on the Gwendraeth at Kidweli, have shown the presence of scarce saltmarsh insects such as the soldier fly *Stratiomys singularior*, the horse fly *Haematopota grandis* and (in brackish ditches on the upper saltmarsh) the scarce blue-tailed damselfly *Ischnura pumilio*. These examples are pointers to the richness of the fauna occurring on the Region's saltmarshes and systematic surveys would surely reveal that the South Wales estuaries contain a broad representation of many of the typical and specialised members of saltmarsh habitats. Throughout the country, our estuaries have suffered degradation from pollution, industrial and agricultural reclamation, and cord grass invasion. New threats continue to present themselves and the Region suffers many pressures on estuarine habitats. Knowledge of the distribution of saltmarsh invertebrate faunas would help to indicate which sections were of greatest conservation importance and therefore assist in developing a strategy to conserve the fullest possible range of saltmarsh wildlife.

Once safeguarded, saltmarshes generally look after themselves, with periodic shifts in the river channel maintaining variety in the successional stages. On the more stable parts of the upper saltmarsh, a tangle of salt-resistant shrubby plants and grasses provides a complex structure for many spiders, beetles and flies to coexist in a natural and very characteristic community. Moderate grazing pressure can easily upset this balance and hence saltmarsh management is generally concerned with preventing access by grazing stock. However, on marshes where there has been a tradition of grazing, the characteristic fauna will have been replaced by species which favour more open ground and in some cases these too can be of conservation value. An outstanding example of this is to be found along the eastern fringe of Whiteford Burrows. Along a line of seepages from the dunes onto the upper saltmarsh, light pony-grazing has maintained an outstanding transitional habitat which is highly regarded for both its plant and animal communities. Poaching damage on the soft peaty sediments keeps this lush fen open and creates pockets of damp mud which are ideal oviposition sites for wetland flies with semi-aquatic larvae. A characteristic insect group of such seepages is the soldier flies and uncommon inhabitants at Whiteford include *Vanoyia tenuicornis*, *Oplodontha viridula*, *Oxycera trilineata* and *Nemotelus notatus*. The Diptera have only been cursorily investigated to date and few other invertebrate orders have received any attention at all but it can be anticipated that additional surveys will reap rich rewards. One speciality known from this strip of seepage marsh is the very rare whorl snail *Vertigo angustior*, known from similar brackish marsh habitat on Oxwich dunes and a few other British sites. The continuation of grazing on this marsh is vital to sustain the structure of the habitat and its species composition and efforts must be made to ensure that stocking levels and grazing patterns do not change substantially in the future.

The upper saltmarsh at Whiteford Burrows yielded a spider new to science in 1964 and subsequently specimens were found on the saltmarsh at Oxwich. *Baryphyma gowerense*, taking its name from the peninsula, was originally thought to be a saltmarsh specialist and was recorded in similar habitat in Co. Kerry, Eire. However, the discovery of this money spider in a valley fen in Norfolk and on flood-meadows in Sweden showed that it was tolerant of a range of wetland conditions, a common trait of several hygrophilous species of spiders. In recent years the Nature Conservancy Council's Welsh Peatland Invertebrate Survey revealed that *B. gowerense* is widely distributed, although still extremely local, on *Molinia*-fens in lowland Wales but in Britain it is still only on the Gower dune systems that the species has been found on saltmarshes.

The majority of the South Wales coastline is 'soft' in geological terms, consisting of dunes and saltmarshes or low cliffs composed of clay deposits. Little is known of the invertebrate fauna of the Region's 'hard' cliffs but information from parts of the Gower Coast and the area around Porthcawl suggests that the Carboniferous Limestone outcrops are of considerable significance for invertebrate conservation. In midsummer the limestone cliffs can be a glorious spectacle of flowers with carpets of thyme and kidney vetch and clumps of bloody crane's-bill. The floral diversity provides sources of nectar and pollen for the vast populations of bees that occur in favoured spots. A combination of factors contributes to the presence of a healthy and varied bee fauna with aspect, substrate and food-sources of chief importance. The cliffs at Horton on the south coast of Gower are an excellent example of prime bee habitat. Here 'head' deposits of periglacial, weathered sand, clay and gravel overlie the hard rock on the lower slopes. This is easily burrowed into and large colonies of species such as *Andrena thoracica* occur in suitable faces. From the cliff-top (with its well-trodden footpath providing additional firm, open ground for other nesting bees and wasps), there is a broad hinterland of lightly-grazed calcareous grassland and mixed scrub, giving extensive foraging opportunities for the aculeates. Along cliff sections where improved pasture abuts the cliff edge there is an obvious reduction in the range and abundance of nectar sources. Some bees can be totally dependent on one species of flower, such as *Andrena hattorfiana* on field scabious, and the larger the area of floriferous grassland on the cliff-top, the greater is their chance of finding enough plants within reach of

a nest-site. Solitary wasps also benefit from similar conditions. For example, *Cerceris arenaria* preys almost exclusively on weevils and the ground around their nesting aggregations can be littered with the bodies of *Otiorhynchus sulcatus* and other related species. To sustain such a population of predators there has to be a rich flora in the vicinity to provide a wealth of prey items. Sadly, over much of Britain, coastal grasslands have been ploughed and re-seeded right up to the cliff edge and it is one of the strengths of the Gower coast that so many cliff sections have a broad belt of semi-natural habitat.

The screes at the foot of the cliffs also support a specialised fauna and in this jumble of rock crevice-dwellers find a stable microclimate that allows them to thrive. A speciality of the Glamorgan coast is the small white woodlouse *Metatrichoniscoides celticus* which lives beneath deeply embedded stones just above the high tide mark. Although presumably overlooked to some extent, it does appear to be genuinely rare and most of its known localities are beneath the limestone cliffs of Glamorgan. Terrestrial invertebrate interest doesn't stop at the tide line, however, as a few species have adapted to occupy air pockets in rock crevices in the intertidal zone. The fauna is sparse but several of its members have a very restricted world distribution. The rocky shores around Swansea, for instance, are home to the ground beetle *Aepus robini* and the shore bug *Aepophilus bonnairei*. They may not face many threats to their habitat yet they are a significant part of our coastal heritage and their conservation is at least deserving of our consideration.

The coastal fringe faces many pressures, presenting a continual challenge to conservationists to keep pace with threats from industry, agriculture, tourism and urban development. The wealth of important wildlife habitats around the South Wales coast demands that the challenge is met and that a future for the abundant diversity of plants, animals and habitats is assured. To conserve this richness in its entirety the fortunes of our coastal invertebrate fauna must also be addressed and to this end entomologists must play their part. There is a need within the Region to identify important localities for the conservation of coastal invertebrates and the small-scale habitat features that are critical to the well-being of valued species. Co-operation between specialists and the conservation organisations is required for informed decisions about management and site-safeguard to be made to the benefit of coastal wildlife as a whole.

Woodlands

Lady Park Wood, Gwent. [Nature Conservancy Council]

Woodlands present the most difficult challenge of all habitats in any attempt to assess the conservation value for invertebrates of one site against another. The problem arises chiefly from the immensity of the potential number of species and the extreme complexity of the woodland habitat, resulting in an incalculable range of niches from the high canopy to the depths of the leaf-litter. No single sampling technique can hope to record more than a fraction of the invertebrate species present in a particular wood and hence it is more or less impossible to develop a quantifiable method of comparing faunas from two different sites. As conservationists, however, we must make judgements on which sites to regard as priorities for site safeguard and management and guidelines must be clear, if not rigid, to enable us to determine where that priority lies. Fortunately, there are many clues in the structure of the woodland habitat to enable us to make preliminary decisions on sites of potential importance and, as many of these features are of common significance to other disciplines of natural history, most of the

important sites are readily recognised by general naturalists with little entomological experience. 'Indicator species' amongst conspicuous groups, such as the butterflies, or easily recorded groups like the molluscs, can also help to suggest which sites are likely to be of importance for a wider range of woodland invertebrates. Unfortunately the general level of invertebrate recording in South Wales woodlands is extraordinarily poor and the Invertebrate Site Register has only been able to identify two sites — the Lower Wye Valley woods and the Oxwich woods on Gower — as being of regional or national significance for invertebrate conservation. This clearly undervalues the overall potential of the Region's woods and the collation of further information will eventually lead to a more realistic appraisal.

As a first principle, the older the woodland the greater is the chance of a full community of characteristic woodland invertebrates being present. Ancient woodlands have had a longer period of time to develop and are therefore more likely to contain a fuller complement of niches, whilst secondary woods also lack the less mobile elements of the fauna which are unable to recolonise after changes in land use. Some of the older South Wales woodlands, such as the upland oakwoods above Abergavenny or the limestone valley woods of the Lower Wye, support snails and slugs including *Leiostyla anglica*, *Limax tenellus* and *L. cinereoniger* which are generally absent from secondary sites because of their poor powers of dispersal.

Management is another time-related factor which can have a strong bearing on the nature of the fauna. Invertebrates generally are very responsive to climatic aspects of their environment and historical continuity of favourable conditions is necessary to maintain the richest assemblages of sensitive species. Traditional coppicing is now a rare practice in Welsh woodlands and as a result many of the species dependent upon the early stages of succession have declined alarmingly. Two characteristic butterflies of the coppice-cycle are the pearl-bordered *Boloria euphrosyne* and high brown *Argynnis adippe* fritillaries, both of which are on the verge of extinction in South Wales. They now occupy a few sites where substantial glades or lightly managed fields on the wood edge provide the right conditions for their larvae to develop on violets. Coppicing maintains a luxuriant ground flora in a sunny but sheltered environment and it is chiefly plant-feeding insects and their predators which are of major conservation interest in such situations. By its very nature, coppicing occurs in a different part of a wood each year and hence the fauna which has adapted to this pattern of management is necessarily mobile to some degree. As coppicing ceased, many species were able to move out into newly-established secondary woods and the young stages of conifer plantations provided an acceptable substitute for some of them. Of course, as the conifers grow increased shading depletes the fauna, but in a few of the older forests with wider-spaced trees and broader rides the edge habitat can sustain a representative diversity of insects for a considerable period. A good example of this is the Corsican pine plantation of Pembrey Forest near Kidweli. The ride systems support an exceptional range of butterflies with strong populations of silver-washed fritillaries *Argynnis paphia* and marbled whites *Melanargia galathea* and the flowery verges are alive with buzzing hoverflies, bees and wasps. Such sites now provide a valuable refuge for open woodland insects but do not compensate for the neglect of traditional coppices. Not all species are capable of long-distance colonisation of available habitat and although many butterflies and moths can make the journey there will be far more species,

like the high brown fritillary, that are doomed to local extinction.

There is a striking contrast between the heavily managed coppice woodland and the primary forest, the wildwood, where trees may live for 500 years before succumbing to old age. We can now only wonder at the wildlife of such places as there is nowhere in Britain that has been left completely free of intervention to follow the natural cycles of decay and regeneration. In a few of the old hunting forests, like Windsor Great Park, Sherwood Forest or the New Forest, we can get an idea of some of the processes involved, but Wales is generally poor in over-mature woodlands and there are no significant sites known in the Region. Invertebrate conservationists are particularly concerned about the saproxylic fauna because it consists of a distinctive assemblage of highly-specialised species that is threatened by habitat loss throughout the country. This threat is difficult to counteract as the fauna is largely hidden and damage can therefore easily be done unwittingly, even by well-intentioned land-managers. The message is slowly getting across but 'tidying-up' of dead or dying timber still takes place on potentially valuable sites and there is a real need within the Region to determine which over-mature woodland habitats deserve protection.

As a tree ages the possibilities for fungal attack in its limbs and trunk increase and the solid timber begins to rot down. This decay can be localised, such as a rot hole in a bough, or more extensive like the breakdown of heartwood by red-rot. Fungal decay is not necessarily the beginning of the end as a solid-rooted maiden or pollard can live for centuries as a hollow shell. Indeed, there is some evidence that fungal activity helps sustain growth by supplying nutrients to the root-system. Decay, or other types of damage to the tree, presents a point of entry for invertebrates into the wood. Very few species are capable of digesting healthy timber and it is dead or dying wood which supports the majority of the specialised inhabitants of old trees. Of these, a high proportion are associated with various forms of fungi or occupy cavities created by fungal breakdown of dead timber.

Although coleopterists in the early part of the century recorded many interesting beetles associated with saproxylic habitats in Gwent and Glamorgan, there is very little site-specific information available today to assist with the identification of important localities. Both of the impressive stag beetles, *Lucanus cervus* and *Dorcus parallelipipedus*, are known from the area and some sites, such as Lady Park Wood in the Wye Valley, and Coed Gwaenydd Bach, Aberdare, have yielded an interesting fauna, including local species such as *Tetratoma fungorum*, *Diplocoelus fagi*, *Colydium elongatum*, and *Tillus elongatus*. Old records of the attractive saproxylic click beetle *Ampedus cinnabarinus* in east Gwent suggest habitats of high quality as one of its two centres of distribution in Britain is in the old woodlands of the Forest of Dean in adjacent Gloucestershire. There are areas of pasture woodland on the slopes of Blorenge and several parklands in the Usk Valley and around Chepstow which would certainly be worth surveying in detail. Unexplored sites probably also occur to the west in Glamorgan but few details are available. In the 1950s and '60s Nicholaston Wood and Oxwich Wood on the Gower were extensively worked by E.A. Fonseca and he recorded a large number of scarce flies associated with old woodlands, including *Coenosia stigmatica*, *Hydrotaea velutina*, *Helina abdominalis*, *Fannia gotlandica*, *F. carbonaria*, *Eustalomyia vittipes*, *Delia tarsifimbria* and *Aulacigaster leucopeza*. It is thought that many of these flies vanished when dead trees were removed around 1960 but at least one of Fonseca's species, the hoverfly *Brachypalpus laphriformis*, is still present today. There has been little comparable recording in the area since Fonseca's studies and it is possible that the Oxwich woodlands retain considerable significance for their saproxylic invertebrates.

Ancient sites with management continuity are, therefore, prime candidates for the conservation of woodland invertebrates. Within each site, features of internal structure, topography, aspect, soil moisture, geology, and the presence of rivers or streams, will add to the diversity of the invertebrate fauna. For instance, rides or glades which allow reasonable amounts of sunshine to flood the woodland edge will benefit many species of bees, wasps, bugs and flies. A varied shrub layer on the glade edges will support a host of woodland moths and the rich flora of grassy rides can support a large and important fauna of plant-feeding beetles, bugs and leaf hoppers. The banks of woodland streams have their own particular faunas, with giant lacewings *Osmylus fulvicephalus* or moss-breeding craneflies such as *Dactylolabis transversata* and *Tipula yerburyi*. The invertebrates of woodlands on acidic or calcareous soils differ markedly, both in terms of the phytophagous species of the different plants occurring in such woods and also the soil and leaf-litter dwelling animals. Aspect, too, can have a pronounced effect, with south-facing woods rich in sun-loving insects and north-facing woods favoured by species with a preference for higher levels of humidity, such as many spiders, or flies with larvae that develop in moist soils.

The conservation of woodland invertebrates needs to take account of this diversity of habitat features to ensure that a representative range of the fauna is safeguarded within the Region. Many such woodlands will already have been conserved on habitat or botanical grounds and as long as management is governed by an understanding of the needs of invertebrates their future should be secure. There is, however, a need to survey sites which may not qualify for conservation on botanical grounds but which support distinctive invertebrate faunas that may not be represented in other woodland types. The over-mature trees of the Region's parklands have already been mentioned but two other areas worthy of concern are open woodlands dominated by wood ants *Formica rufa* and long-established carr woodlands of alder and willow.

Giant lacewing *Osmylus fulvicephalus*. [R.S. Key]

In parts of North Wales *Formica lugubris* is abundant in conifer plantations but *F. rufa*-dominated deciduous woodlands are scarce in Wales. These ants exert tremendous ecological pressure on the constituents of their woodland home and through their predation create a unique community of woodland invertebrates, which in turn affects the balance of the flora around them. This is of considerable scientific interest and deserves recognition by the conservation organisations. There is also a suite of commensal invertebrates which inhabit the nests of wood ants and require conservation in their own right. From the records available it would appear that wood ants are scarce in South Wales and efforts should be made to ensure that at least the largest surviving colonies are safeguarded.

Carr woodland is often regarded as 'secondary' and dismissed unless there is an associated ground flora of some interest. In fact, in waterlogged sites carr can be more or less self perpetuating and where carr has been present for a considerable time there will probably also be an important range of invertebrates feeding on the foliage, breeding in rotten willow branches or bracket fungi, lurking amongst the tussocks beneath the trees, or breeding in pools amongst the wet soil. There is a good example on the banks of the Afon Honddu in Gwent where old alders stand on the alluvial sediments derived from Old Red Sandstone. The very scarce cranefly *Nephrotoma lunulicornis* has been recorded along

with the soldier fly *Oxycera terminalis*, a Red Data Book species known chiefly from riverbanks in the southern Welsh Borders. These species are characteristic of good quality riparian woodland and there are many other invertebrates from a wide range of orders which predominantly occur in carr and their conservation also needs to be taken into account when considering woodland habitats in need of formal protection.

There is a great deal of variety in the woodland types present in South Wales Region and the overall potential for invertebrate conservation is equally strong. The coastal dingles of the Vale of Glamorgan, the gorge woodlands of the Taff and the Wye, the acid oakwoods of the northern hills, the chain of beechwoods across the limestone belt, the cliff woodlands of the Gower, riverside carr along the Usk and the Monnow, the parklands of Gwent: a rich diversity of habitats which undoubtedly shelters an important selection of woodland invertebrates in need of conservation. Yet even woodlands like Cwm Clydach National Nature Reserve, with its splendid valleyside beeches at the western edge of their native British range, has had precious little entomological survey. The comparative neglect of the Region's wooded habitats by invertebrate zoologists in recent times needs to be reversed in order that priorities for conservation can be identified. There is much that the entomologist can do to assist with woodland conservation in South Wales and plenty of scope for rewarding fieldwork in a varied range of quality habitats.

Lowland heaths and grasslands

Welsh Moor, West Glamorgan. [A.P. Fowles]

Although there are a few localities on the Gower peninsula where there are surviving tracts of dry heather moor (particularly Clyne Common and Rhossili Down), it is much more common for the heaths of the Region to be part of an intimate mosaic of unimproved heathy grassland, flushes and small mires. For this reason it is more convenient to discuss the features of invertebrate interest for these two habitat formations in one chapter, but it is also true that these sites are largely indivisable and, to some extent, share similar faunas. The chief factor behind this juxtaposition of heaths and pastures in South Wales is that practically all of the existing heathlands are now to be found on the grazed commons of Gower. The commons are permanently grazed by a variety of goats, ponies, cattle and sheep and most are also burnt on a two or three year rotation to provide 'early bite'. This produces a patchwork of acidic grasslands and heather-dominated communities of some interest for invertebrates, though regular burning sadly reduces their overall value for conservation.

It is a curious fact that grasslands throughout Britain have generally received little attention from invertebrate zoologists, with the notable exception of the chalk and limestone grasslands of southern England. We revere our semi-natural pastures and meadows for their botanical diversity and of all habitat types it is the lowland grasslands that are regularly highlighted for their rate of loss and hence are at the forefront of many a conservation battle. Yet apart from the obligatory list of butterflies and perhaps a few notes on grasshoppers and a few other conspicuous insects, there is generally a lack of information and understanding regarding even the commonest components of the grassland invertebrate community. This position prevails throughout Wales but is particularly acute in South Wales where, on the basis of information collated for the Invertebrate Site Register, next to nothing is known of the invertebrate communities inhabiting the Region's grasslands. If we are to conserve the whole spectrum of wildlife found in meadows and pastures, rather than just maintain the botanical richness, then this situation must change. Grasslands are the most managed of all habitat types, requiring constant interference with natural succession if they are to retain their importance for wildlife. Alterations to the management regime usually result in a rapid change in micro-climate at sward level and this can have a devastating effect on the resident invertebrate fauna. If we are to manage our grasslands in a manner that is compatible with their characteristic invertebrates then we need to have a more detailed knowledge of the species that make up the fauna and an indication of their basic ecological requirements. At present we rely on continuing traditional management, without always knowing what that entails, and face difficulties when ownerships change or agricultural trends shift away from established patterns. Much more needs to be learnt about the levels of grazing and types of stock which produce the structural mosaics crucial for the well-being of plants and animals on our unimproved grasslands.

We are on slightly firmer ground with regard to knowledge of the principles of heathland management as these have been the subject of many ecological surveys. However, most of these studies have been carried out on the dry heaths of southern England which are very different from the wet and humid heaths of Wales. Burning is an accepted, though somewhat contentious, management tool on some of these dry heaths, where the stated aim is to control scrub invasion and bracken encroachment and to vary the age structure of the heather stands. Although spring fires are a traditional agricultural practice on the wet heaths of Wales, such a drastic form of management should only be used as a last resort on conservation sites as fires can have a devastating effect on the faunas of wet peat and soil. Invasive plants are much less of a problem here and they can invariably be controlled by sensible stocking levels. As with grasslands, there is no substitute for the correct use of grazing stock, taking care to ensure that the right type of animal (usually ponies or cattle) grazes at the right time of year. The best compromise is for light grazing throughout the year, although stock may have to be removed during the winter when the fields are too wet or there is insufficient forage. Domestic stock at moderate densities will produce a natural patchwork in the heath or grassland by selectively cropping the most palatable areas of sward. This creates exactly the kind of mosaic of vegetation structures, including dense heath, pockets of scrub, tussocks, short turf, and patches of bare peat or poached mud, that are so crucial to the invertebrates of heathlands or grasslands.

Management objectives in these habitats should begin with the principle of avoiding uniformity at all cost.

Within South Wales there are two major concentrations of unimproved heaths and pastures — the Gower commons and the mesotrophic grasslands of the West Glamorgan Coal Measures. In both of these areas one of the main benefits to invertebrate conservation is the extent and proximity of suitable habitat, considerably lessening the chances of local extinction by increasing the possibilities of recolonisation. We are fortunate in Wales that certain districts have retained such large areas of semi-natural grazings and conservationists should aim to preserve as much of these as possible. Individual populations of invertebrates wax and wane naturally in response to climatic conditions, foodplant shortages and parasite/predator cycles, and management catastrophes (such as neglect or intensification of grazing) can be the final straw. If this happens on isolated sites then there is little chance of the affected species returning to establish new populations but with adjacent reservoirs of semi-natural habitat there is hope for the future.

Such local extinctions are well documented for the marsh fritillary *Eurodryas aurinia* and one of the main reasons for the strength of the colonies in Dyfed and Glamorgan is the inter-change between populations that is possible in the wealth of suitable sites across its range. The marsh fritillary is undoubtedly the best-known grassland invertebrate of the Region and the importance of the Gower colonies has long been recognised. It is only in recent years that the quality of the Coal Measures grasslands has been identified and here, too, there are strong populations of marsh fritillaries. These pastures are an eastern extension of the acclaimed whorled caraway meadows of Carmarthenshire and, being part of the same ecological unit, they will have similar elements of the fauna. Along with the marsh fritillaries there are small pearl-bordered fritillaries *Boloria selene* and marbled whites *Melanargia galathea* and undoubtedly a host of other phytophagous insects waiting to be discovered. These will include some of the scarcer beetles known from the Gower commons, such as the flea beetle *Longitarsus holsaticus*, which feeds on louseworts, or the metallic-blue jewel beetle *Trachys troglodytes* on devil's-bit scabious. Purple moor-grass is an important constituent of many Welsh grasslands and, in addition to supporting the uncommon leaf hopper *Sorhoanus xanthoneurus*, its tussocks and leaf-litter provide shelter for a vast array of grassland invertebrates during inclement weather.

Pont Croesor, Gwynedd: The Glaslyn River has several areas of valuable carr and other wetland habitats on its banks. These riverside fens and swamps support a rich invertebrate fauna that is dependent upon the high water table provided by the adjacent river.
(Photograph by A.P. Fowles.)

Bosherston Lakes, Dyfed: The beautiful marl lakes of Stackpole National Nature Reserve are home to many scarce freshwater invertebrates.
(Photograph by A.P. Fowles.)

Llyn Tegid, Gwynedd: Llyn Tegid is the largest natural lake in Wales and formerly supported a large population of the glutinous snail *Myxas glutinosa*, a species which has declined alarmingly throughout Britain and may now be extinct in Wales.
(Photograph by A.P. Fowles.)

Cadair Idris, Gwynedd: The corrie lake of Llyn Cau is typical of the upland water bodies of Snowdonia. They generally contain relatively few species of invertebrate but their cold, nutrient-poor waters are a refuge for glacial relicts and of interest for their unique species-assemblages.
(Photograph by A.P. Fowles.)

Cors Fochno, Dyfed: Ditches cut as firebreaks into the peat at the edge of this raised mire are important for dragonflies, particularly the small red damselfly *Ceriagrion tenellum*.
(Photograph by R.P. Bray.)

***Eugraphe subrosea* (Lepidoptera):** Believed extinct in Britain for more than a hundred years, the rosy marsh moth was discovered in Wales in 1965. A large population is present on Cors Fochno in Cardiganshire, where the caterpillars feed mainly on bog myrtle.
(Photograph by P. Waring.)

Fenn's Moss, Clwyd: Traditional peat-cutting on this superb raised mire complex maintains pockets of bare peat and open water for a variety of uncommon peatland invertebrates.
(Photograph by NCC.)

***Leucorrhinia dubia* (Odonata):** The only locality in Wales for the white-faced darter is Fenn's Moss in Denbighshire. Here this scarce dragonfly occupies pools in the raised mire which have been created by traditional peat-cutting.
(Photograph by J. Porter.)

Marbled white *Melanargia galathea*.
[A.P. Fowles]

Unimproved calcareous grasslands are generally scarce in south Wales, particularly as so much of the Carboniferous Limestone of the Gower is masked by deep glacial deposits. The few sites which do survive probably contain valuable invertebrate faunas involving many orders and with a high proportion of species having a restricted distribution in Wales. This is due in part to the different flora occurring on limestone and also to the dry, calcareous soils which are texturally and chemically so different from the predominating peats and clays of the Region. Surveys of the beetles, flies, moths, bugs, snails and spiders of such sites are long overdue and entomologists should be directed to localities such as Old Castle Down in Mid Glamorgan or Brockwell's Meadows in Gwent. Records of marbled whites, dark green fritillaries *Argynnis aglaja*, brown argus *Aricia agestis*, and great green bush crickets *Tettigonia viridissima* indicate potential but hardly tell the full story. Calcareous grasslands are as much in need of sensitive management as any other habitat and the assistance of entomologists in the compilation of management plans could be of great value.

Brockwell's Meadows are a series of unimproved pastures and hay meadows on lime-rich soils overlying Carboniferous Limestone and Triassic sandstone and are chiefly of importance for their population of *Asilus crabroniformis*, the hornet robber fly. This impressive creature (a convincing mimic of the hornet when in flight) is a reminder of the dependence of invertebrates on the continuance of traditional agricultural practices. Its larvae are predators of the inhabitants of cow-pats, the fly and beetle larvae which break down dung and return the nutrients to the soil. After developing to maturity, the *Asilus* larva pupates in the free-draining soils of unimproved pastures and then emerges in mid-summer as the adult robber fly to hunt for grasshoppers and other prey. It has an obvious requirement for the presence of cow-pats (or horse-dung sometimes suffices) of the right age in which to lay its eggs and the removal of grazing stock for just one season can lead to its extinction. *Asilus* has disappeared from many of its former haunts in southern England as heaths and pastures have been ploughed up or cattle replaced by sheep. It is a conspicuous insect and not likely to be overlooked by the observant naturalist and so the handful of sites currently known in Wales is probably a true reflection of its rarity. Another uncommon member of the dung community is the beetle *Aphodius porcus*, which has been recorded at Fairwood Common on the Gower. This species is a parasite in the burrows of dor beetle larvae *Geotrupes* spp. and is a further example of the intricate web of species associated with the presence of grazing stock.

A problem which is familiar to many conservation organisations is the difficulty in persuading graziers to rent pasturage on unimproved grasslands. This is most acute in arable districts where there may simply be no animals available and mowing may be the only alternative to prevent coarse grasses dominating valuable forb-rich swards. There is no easy solution to this dilemma because mowing is unquestionably a disastrous event for the majority of grassland invertebrates. Mowing causes the sudden loss of shelter, food and breeding sites which can devastate invertebrate populations and the removal of nectar sources may even affect species from adjacent habitats. This is the reason why hay meadows are invariably poor habitats for invertebrates as it is only species which live and breed below cutting height that can usually persist from year to year. If it is absolutely necessary to mow grasslands that are not traditional hay meadows then a system of rotation should be adopted whereby a maximum of a quarter of the field should be cut in any one year. This should be sufficient to prevent major deterioration of the botanical composition of the sward whilst maintaining sufficient foodplants in the right stages for breeding invertebrates. In this way leaf-feeding caterpillars, the bugs, beetles, and micro-moths of seed-heads, and the stem-breeding bees of woody plants will suffer only partial extinction.

The struggle to conserve the richest features of our natural heritage means that effort and resources are invariably spread thin and all too often it is those habitats that are in need of continual up-keep that suffer first. In this respect, grasslands are the most critical habitat type as they are most responsive to changes in management, relaxation leading to rapid alterations in micro-environments. Heathlands are more robust but nonetheless requiring of regular management input if they are to retain their ecological diversity. The semi-natural pastures and commons of lowland South Wales are of great potential value for the conservation of invertebrate assemblages which are declining over so much of England and Wales. This wealth should not be squandered and there is a duty on all concerned to ensure that the delights of the living grasslands — the butterflies, bees, grasshoppers and flowers — continue to be among the natural treasures of South Wales.

Open water and its margins

River Monnow, Gwent. [A.P. Fowles]

Stretching for 30 km along the coast of Gwent, on both sides of the mouth of the River Usk, is a vast expanse of flat pasture that constitutes one of the most important aquatic habitats in Wales. At first sight these monotonous green fields seem an unlikely candidate for such an accolade but these fields are surrounded by 'water-fences', an estimated 1400 km of open ditches, or 'reens' as they are known locally. The Gwent Levels are man-made in every sense, owing their existence to the construction of the sea wall that prevents tidal flooding on the former alluvial marsh, and the ditches are regularly cleaned to fulfill their roles of conveying drainage water, preventing stock from straying, and providing drinking water for horses and cattle. This cycle of maintenance is crucial to the wildlife value of the reens and the significance of the Gwent Levels is due chiefly to the related factors of their extent and their varied management.

Although there are a number of small areas of grazing marsh around the coast of Wales, notably on Anglesey, the Gwent Levels are without parallel in the Principality and are matched in national terms only by the Thames marshes of Essex and North Kent, the Somerset Moors and Levels, the marshes of Norfolk Broadland and Pevensey Levels in Sussex. These areas have many similarities amongst their floras and faunas but there are also differences brought about by water chemistry and geography that makes each unique and of the greatest importance for nature conservation. The Gwent Levels are chiefly located on alluvial clays, with a small area of fen peat around Magor. Back ditches, those immediately behind the sea wall, are influenced by saline incursions but in general the ditches are less brackish than the North Kent marshes, for instance, and halophilous species form only a small proportion of the total fauna. An additional bonus of the Gwent Levels is the profusion of hedges and willow pollards, adding to the diversity of habitat and providing shelter for aerial insects. None of the other major grazing marshes has anything like the extent of hedged ditches here and hence this is a distinctive and valuable characteristic of the area.

Management is crucial to the wildlife of the

ditch system. One of the main reasons why the Gwent Levels supports such a wide range of scarce aquatic and semi-aquatic invertebrates is the tri-partite regime which controls the drainage network. An essential operation in ditch management is dredging, which involves re-profiling the ditch bottom to remove the silts and mats of vegetation that build up over a number of years. Without dredging, a ditch no longer performs its functions as a fence, drain, or source of drinking water and it is therefore vital to the grazier that dredging is carried out on a regular basis. On a small tract of grazing marsh this may be undertaken all at once, say every five years, or larger sites may have some of their ditches cleared annually on rotation every five years. This limits the stages in hydroseral succession available to the ditch invertebrates and favours species of open water to the detriment of the fauna of partially choked drains. On the Gwent Levels, as with the other major sites, the drainage cycles are more varied and ditches representing the full hydroseral succession are available annually. This is facilitated by having three different bodies of responsibility for ditch management — the Welsh Water Authority, the Internal Drainage Board and the graziers themselves — which in practice results in three different cycles of management. The Water Authority are responsible for a series of main drains, broad canal-like ditches whose purpose is to carry water from the surrounding catchment down to the sluices and out to sea. After dredging, the steady build-up of aquatic and emergent vegetation begins to hinder the flow of water and hence main drains are dredged on a three to five year cycle. The Internal Drainage Board takes care of ditches whose chief purpose is to drain water off the Levels fields themselves and maintain the grazings to an agricultural standard. Their ditches are usually dredged every seven or eight years and therefore contain substantially more vegetation than the main drains before they are cleared out. The remaining ditches, known as minor or subsidiary ditches, are dredged according to the grazier's needs. These vary from field to field but some may be left for fifteen years before dredging, by which time they are more or less choked by reed, reedmace and other tall emergents. Orchestrating such a regime within a management plan would be an impossible task but the combination of management regimes employed for drainage and agricultural reasons inadvertently maintains the habitats of the ditch wildlife.

Studies by the Nature Conservancy Council in 1985 identified distinct communities of invertebrates associated with the different types of drain and the stage that the drain had reached in the hydroseral succession. Although several rare species provide important exceptions to the rule, in general the trend was for the open water of the main drains to be of greatest value for aquatic invertebrates and partially-choked ditches to be best for semi-aquatic invertebrates. This may seem self-evident as many semi-aquatic species are associated with particular foodplants but there are also aquatic species which live amongst submerged or floating plants and there are also terrestrial beetles, flies and bugs which inhabit the damp margins of open ditches. The real truth is that to conserve the fullest representation of the Levels fauna all conditions need to be present within the ditch network, from deep open water to floating mats of duckweed and solid stands of reed or reed sweet-grass. There is the additional factor on the Gwent Levels that, as far as possible, these conditions also need to be replicated on both the peat and clay substrates as each supports a number of species not found in other areas.

More than a hundred scarce invertebrate species have been recorded from the Levels, the majority being characteristic of such habitats or of areas of open water in fens. One of the rarest nationally is the soldier fly *Odontomyia ornata* which, apart from a few records from East Anglia, is more or less confined to the Gwent and Somerset Levels. The larvae develop amongst aquatic vegetation, most frequently mats of duckweed, and are usually found in ditches which have been cleared out relatively recently. *O. ornata* is widespread on the Gwent Levels, appearing to favour the broader ditches. Another soldier fly, the local *Stratiomys singularior*, is also widely-distributed on the Gwent Levels and is probably the host for the very rare parasitic wasp *Chalcis sispes*. This highly distinctive hymenopteran is known only from coastal levels (with a stronghold on the North Kent marshes) and breeds only on the larvae of flies of the genus *Stratiomys*. As *Stratiomys* spp. are invariably scarce and dependent on good quality habitats, it follows that the parasite itself is a threatened species. *Thrypticus tarsalis*, a small fly whose larvae are leaf-miners of tall grasses and sedges in fens, and the 'big-headed fly' *Tomosvaryella minima*, a parasite of leaf hoppers, are other rare Diptera that have been recorded.

The water beetle assemblage on the Gwent Levels is unique in Wales, including a strong population of the great silver water beetle *Hydrophilus piceus*. *Haliplus mucronatus*, occurring here and on the grazing marshes at Margam Moors south-east of Port Talbot, is a coastal species usually found in brackish pools and ditches. There are also a number of water beetles recorded here which are not known elsewhere in Wales, including *Peltodytes caesus*, *Hydaticus transversalis*, *Limnoxenus niger* and *Berosus affinis*. The dragonfly fauna is typically rich with good numbers of the hairy dragonfly *Brachytron pratense*, the variable damselfly *Coenagrion pulchellum* and other local species such as the emperor dragonfly *Anax imperator* and the black-tailed skimmer *Orthetrum cancellatum*. The reens support a good diversity of freshwater molluscs which are scarce in Wales, including the swan mussel *Anodonta cygnaea* and the great ramshorn *Planorbarius corneus*. The pea mussel *Pisidium pseudosphaerium* is a national rarity which inhabits choked ditches and ponds. The long rotation of ditch management on the subsidiary reens of the Gwent Levels is vital for its survival here.

The formal notification of the Gwent Levels as a Site of Special Scientific Interest has been a major but thoroughly justified task. This unique area now has strong safeguards against the threats of industrial development that loomed large from Newport. The continuing importance of the Levels now depends on sustained cooperation between conservationists and those responsible for the upkeep of the ditch system and its water quality. Undoubtedly there will be problems on such a large area over the years to come and changing agricultural trends may disrupt the balance of the management cycle but the efforts to conserve this outstanding site are surely worthwhile.

Lying mainly to the east of the South Wales coalfield, Gwent is also fortunate to contain three exceptional rivers within its borders — the Monnow, Usk and Wye. Industry and its attendant pollution tainted all of the major watercourses in Glamorgan and West Gwent and, whilst these are improving steadily, there is no evidence as yet that they have regained representative faunas. Further west, in the Llanelli Borough of Dyfed, the Gwendraeth Fach is highly regarded by the Institute of Freshwater Ecology but only a short stretch is within South Wales Region and there is no data available on the interest of this section. The three Gwent rivers, however, are all excellent examples of watercourses with good water-quality and little bank or channel modification. The Wye is, of course, the best known of these and the picturesque valley between Monmouth and Chepstow, with its steep wooded banks and broad sheets of sparkling water-crowfoot across the main river, is one of the most outstanding natural features of the Region. The Wye has been the subject of many freshwater studies and its

fauna of mayflies, caddisflies, riffle beetles, etc. is indicative of its clean water and varied river-bed and riparian habitats. Unfortunately, little of this work seems to have been carried out in the Gwent stretch of the river and we can only surmise that the rich assemblages of species known from places such as Symonds Yat upstream in Herefordshire also occur in South Wales. We do know that the club-tailed dragonfly *Gomphus vulgatissimus*, the white-legged damselfly *Platycnemis pennipes* and the rare mayfly *Potamanthus luteus* occur in the Wye Valley gorge. All of these are indicators of good river quality but more information on the fauna of the lower Wye would be of interest.

The Usk is similarly neglected and requires modern surveys but, on the basis of knowledge of the state of the river, it is likely to be comparable to the Monnow for its importance in a Welsh context. For much of its course in Gwent the Usk meanders through a fertile floodplain, depositing sandy shoals on the inner curve of its broad sweeps and cutting into the earth banks on its outer edge. Much of the floodplain is grazed, with cattle having access to the banks, and their trampling can damage important invertebrate habitats. However, there are untrampled shoals and there are also pockets of willow and alder carr on the sandy alluvium. A highly-specialised invertebrate fauna inhabits such riverside deposits, consisting chiefly of beetles and flies, and the craneflies are a group which are particularly well-represented. Many of the best sites for riverbank craneflies are on the untamed rivers of Scotland but the Usk is one of the best in England and Wales with such species as *Erioptera limbata*, *Gonomyia abbreviata*, *Limonia omissinervis* and *Rhabdomastix hilaris*. Each of these is a Red Data Book species known from very few sites nationally and they all breed in damp sand on the banks of rivers or streams, usually in the shade of willow or alders. The occurrence of all four of these species at the same site, near Newbridge-on-Usk, is quite exceptional.

By contrast, the Monnow's fauna is well-documented (although much remains to be done) and there is no question that this is an outstanding river system. Approaching the riverbank, the abundance of white-legged damselflies and banded demoiselles *Calopteryx splendens* is a sign that this is high quality habitat and a glance at the well-aerated water rushing across riffles through tree-lined banks, or sluggishly flowing through deep river-bed pools between sandy cliffs and shoals, readily confirms this impression. The diversity of its aquatic fauna is very high for a Welsh river with at least twenty species of mayfly, including *Ephemerella notata* and a good range of stoneflies and caddisflies. The aquatic Diptera include the rare *Atrichops crassipes*, both species of *Atherix* and the riverbank stiletto flies *Psilocephala rustica* and *Thereva lunulata*. The Monnow is a stronghold for the soldier fly *Oxycera terminalis*, which is associated with tree-lined riverbanks, and the range of dance flies (Empididae) recorded is exceptional. The empids *Tachydromia halidayi*, *T. woodi*, *T. costalis* and *Empis limata* are amongst the nationally rare members of the family known from the Monnow. As with the Usk, the cranefly fauna is outstanding and there are two species — *Erioptera pusilla* and *Gonomyia punctata* — which were found on the banks of the Monnow in the early part of this century but have not been seen anywhere in Britain since then. There is every chance that they are still present somewhere along the Monnow. The sandy banks support several rare beetles, most notably the black and yellow click beetle *Negastrius sabulicola* which has its British headquarters on the rivers of mid and south-east Wales. The ground beetles *Bembidion littorale* and *Amara fulva* and the rove beetles *Philonthus atratus*, *P. rotundicollis* and *P. rubripennis* are all scarce inhabitants of sandy riverbanks which are known from the Monnow Valley. Finally there are the riffle beetles, aquatic species that live under stones or amongst vegetation on the river bed, only leaving the

water to pupate on the riverbank. They are very good indicators of water quality and the total of eight species is probably not exceeded elsewhere in Wales. *Riolus cupreus*, *R. subviolaceus* and *Oulimnius troglodytes* are nationally scarce but *Normandia nitens* is restricted entirely to the Wye, the Teme and the Monnow.

Standing water habitats, such as lakes and ponds, are not common in the Region as a whole, although there is a concentration of moorland pools on the Gower commons. There is no information to suggest that any of the known sites is of especial importance for invertebrates, with the notable exception of a shallow pool in Pembrey Forest, Dyfed. Although surrounded by conifers and owing its existence to the excavation of an old dune slack, this shallow pool has an extraordinary diversity of snail-killing flies. The larvae of these flies feed upon aquatic and semi-aquatic snails and seem to prefer sites where the snails are frequently stranded on the water margin by falling water levels. This is a typical event at Pembrey and the base-enriched waters promote a healthy abundance and variety of water snails. So far nineteen species of snail-killing fly have been recorded, including a high proportion of nationally scarce species such as *Pteromicra leucopeza* and *Sciomyza simplex*.

Other noteworthy sites include the flooded limestone quarries at Cosmeston Country Park and the dune pool at Kenfig Burrows. Both of these sites have good dragonfly faunas including the hairy dragonfly, the variable damselfly, the scarce blue-tailed damselfly *Ischnura pumilio* and the ruddy darter *Sympetrum sanguineum*. Kenfig Pool is the largest natural body of standing freshwater in Glamorgan and its mixed marginal habitats of marsh, carr and sandy banks are likely to support a number of uncommon invertebrates, though there is little data available on the marginal fauna. The aquatic invertebrates have been sampled and comprise a broad range of common species along with a few localised species such as the lesser water boatman *Corixa panzeri*. The Gower ponds are similarly inhabited by an assemblage of common aquatic invertebrates and many, like Broad Pool on Cefn Bryn, support a reasonable selection of dragonflies. It is likely that these ponds are more important for the invertebrates of their pony-trampled margins as the damp, peaty soils of pond edges are a valuable habitat for invertebrates. In the 1950s and 1960s E.A. Fonseca recorded a host of rare flies from the Gower commons, many of which (in families such as the Tabanidae, Dolichopodidae and Muscidae) have larvae which breed in damp soil. It is not generally possible to localise these

Cluster of *Atherix ibis*. [R.S. Key]

records to specific ponds and it would be useful to have a modern study of the Diptera of the Gower ponds.

Disused canals are effectively standing water bodies as aquatic vegetation impedes the normally slight water-flow. There are a number of canal systems in the Region, some of which are of high botanical interest, and these provide a potentially valuable resource for aquatic and water-margin invertebrates. The Tennant Canal east of Swansea has a superb fen flora and should prove to be an excellent site for invertebrates. Other examples are the Glamorgan Canal on the Taff north-west of Cardiff and the Monmouth and Brecon Canal following the course of the Usk. Neglected canals, like the ditch systems that began this discussion on freshwater habitats in south Wales, have a limited life span as sediment builds up and the rafts of vegetation creep out from either bank. To maintain

biological diversity and the significance of such sites for freshwater conservation, periodic clearance is essential. It would be useful to have much more detailed information on the invertebrates of the standing water bodies of potential conservation importance in order to guide management. For instance, the shore of Kenfig Pool used to be mainly open sand, a juxtaposition which is a very valuable dune habitat. Natural succession has seen the spread of reed and willow such that the limited lengths of open bank are now heavily trampled by visiting tourists. If there had been information available on the sandy shore fauna it might have been possible to conserve and manage a suitable stretch. Perhaps the specialised inhabitants still linger on in a quiet bay but, as with all semi-natural habitats, without recognition of features of importance for invertebrates the fate of scarce species is uncertain.

Lowland peatlands

Crymlyn Bog, West Glamorgan. [A.P. Fowles]

Away from the coast, the best-known habitat formation for invertebrates in South Wales is the complex of fens and mires that constitute the peatland resource. Some of the larger sites, such as Crymlyn Bog, have been famous for their entomological interest for much of this century, but it is the Nature Conservancy Council's Welsh Peatland Invertebrate Survey (WPIS) that has enabled a broader assessment to be made of the quality and range of the peatland invertebrate fauna in the Region. WPIS investigated fifteen sites in 1988 and 1989, including basin mires, flush systems and valley fens. The results are not fully analysed at present, but preliminary studies indicate some of the habitat associations of peatland invertebrates that will be applicable to other sites in the Region that were not sampled during this survey.

Peatlands are usually classified broadly in terms of the topographical or hydrological features which combine to give rise to the waterlogged conditions that slow down the decay of plant material and hence allow peat to form. Differences in the nutrient-status of the water

supply can account for much of the variation in peatland vegetation, whilst current or historical management can also affect the structure of the site and the plants and animals that thrive there. Although the broad-scale classification is a useful descriptive tool it is apparent that invertebrates in peatland habitats are linked more closely to the plant structure and trophic status of a site than to topographical features. For example, the faunas of a calcareous basin fen and valley fen will have much more in common than the faunas of an acid valley fen and a calcareous valley fen. Host-specific phytophagous insects are obviously dependent on the presence of their particular foodplant but otherwise peatland invertebrates chiefly vary according to the complexity of the vegetation structure, the height of the water-table and the chemical composition of the groundwater.

For invertebrate conservation, the most important aspect of the peatland resource in South Wales is the diversity and extent of the rich fens along the coastal belt. These contain examples of wetland vegetation communities

104

which are better represented here than elsewhere in Wales and they display affinities amongst their invertebrate assemblages with the fens of south-east England and East Anglia. For their rarity in a Welsh context and their ecological importance as geographically-isolated outliers of the English fens, they are of high conservation value and the conservation of the remaining undamaged examples is a priority. The extensive fenland complex of Crymlyn Bog and Pant-y-Sais on the edge of Swansea is an outstanding example of the richness of such habitats and supports an invertebrate fauna of comparable significance. One of the main reasons for this is the extraordinary diversity of peatland habitats contained within its 260 ha, the largest area of lowland fen in Wales. Thus, there are pockets of *Sphagnum* mire and poor-fen, reedswamp, sedge fen and wet heath, some of which is cattle-grazed and the rest unmanaged. Each of these areas has its own interest but it is probably the tall fens of common reed, reed sweet-grass and various sedges that are most important for invertebrates.

The dense tangle of tall fen communities has, in simplified terms, two basic habitats for invertebrates — the aerial structures of stems and leaves and the slowly-decaying litter of previous years' growth on the ground. The thick stems of plants such as common reed, reed sweet-grass and reedmace offer a protected environment for the larvae of various flies, moths and beetles in which they can develop to maturity in relative safety from predators. Uncommon moths of such fens include the twin-spotted wainscot *Archanara geminipuncta*, brown-veined wainscot *A. dissoluta* and Webb's wainscot *A. sparganii*, each of which have larvae which mine the stems of tall fenland plants. A number of hoverflies are characteristic inhabitants, their larvae often occurring amongst plant roots, and at Crymlyn *Anasimyia transfuga* and *Parhelophilus consimilis* are of particular note. These species occur where the fen is flooded. Another aquatic denizen of reed roots is the reed beetle *Plateumaris braccata*, known from several fens along the South Wales coast but otherwise rare in Wales. The soldier beetle *Silis ruficollis* has a stronghold in South Wales but is otherwise chiefly known from East Anglia. It is entirely restricted to tall fen habitats and is one of the specialities of the Region's peatlands. *Cantharis thoracica* is another predatory soldier beetle which is typical of reedswamp and several spiders of the genus *Clubiona* can be found on their silken retreats made from reed leaves drawn together. *Marpissa radiata*, a jumping spider, spins its cocoon amongst the flowerheads but also hunts amongst the dense litter at ground level. Most of

its records are from the East Anglian fens but it has recently been discovered on Crymlyn Bog.

Damp, decaying leaf-litter provides the micro-habitat for the larvae of many wetland flies. The cranefly *Erioptera squalida*, for instance, is associated with *Glyceria* fens. Predatory flies are also to be found here, such as the snail-killing fly *Antichaeta analis* which breeds on the egg-capsules of aquatic snails. The pretty ground beetle *Odacantha melanura* hunts amongst the stems of fenland plants and is very rare in Wales, although fairly widespread in the fens of southern England. Light grazing opens up the fen and trampling breaks down the litter-layer such that bare peat is exposed. This change in the micro-climate at ground level has a significant effect on the fauna and accommodates a host of species that cannot penetrate dense stands of reeds and sedges. Ground beetles are an obvious component of such open fens and typical members of the fauna include *Blethisa multipunctata*, *Oodes helopioides* and *Chlaenius nigricornis*. The wolf spider *Pirata piscatorius* is also characteristic of grazed fens, along with a suite of invertebrates, such as rove beetles and dance flies, which occur on wet peat at the edges of pools.

Crymlyn Bog represents a classic example of the South Wales tall fens but they are widespread in the Region and, without exception, where they have been the subject of some degree of entomological survey they have been found to contain much of interest. The Llanelli Borough of Carmarthenshire has three main sites which effectively mark the western limit of these invertebrate communities as similar fens elsewhere in Dyfed appear to lack most of the 'East Anglian' species. Ffrwd Farm near Kidweli is a comparatively small rich fen but nonetheless contains an interesting fauna with many of the species mentioned above, including *Silis ruficollis* at the edge of its range. The marginal fens of Machynys Ponds are even smaller but this important site still supports a distinctive fenland fauna with many scarce species amongst its beetles, hoverflies, soldier flies, etc. The additional presence of an excellent dragonfly fauna, which includes the hairy dragonfly *Brachytron pratense*, makes this a significant site in a Regional context and as its future has been under considerable threat from urban development it is hoped that efforts to conserve it will succeed. Also on the edge of Llanelli, and hence under continual threat from urban expansion, are the reedswamps of the Bynea area. This is little-known entomologically at present but the reed beetle *Plateumaris braccata* occurs and moth-trapping has yielded local species such as the obscure wainscot *Mythimna obsoleta* and the silky

Reed beetle *Plateumaris braccata*
[R.S. Key]

wainscot *Chilodes maritimus*. Much of this area has been fragmented by reclamation and development and as the remnants constitute some of the best coastal tall fen in Dyfed they should be surveyed in more detail with a view to formal protection.

The best of the Gower fens is at Oxwich Bay where former grazing marsh has developed into mixed tall fen after drains fell into disrepair. It is an important constituent of the Oxwich complex and supports a typical fen fauna along with rarities such as the cranefly *Erioptera meijerei*, which is not known to occur elsewhere in Wales. In the east of the Region, Magor Marsh is the last surviving remnant of the once extensive fenlands on the alluvium deposits of the Gwent coast. Dissected by internal drainage ditches, the compartments vary in character from ungrazed reedswamp to heavily-grazed fen meadow. The differences in the fauna of the managed and unmanaged fields is marked and the variation in vegetation structure due to management contributes significantly to the invertebrate diversity. The grazed fen has a rich carabid and staphylinid fauna with *Tachys bistriatus*, *Pterostichus anthracinus*, *Stenus assequens* and *Paederus fuscipes* of particular note. These species are more or less absent from ungrazed tall fen, where *Paederus riparius* replaces its scarcer congener, but the uncommon rove beetles *Platystethus nodifrons* and *Stenus palustris* are frequent. By contrast, the ungrazed fens are richer for fenland Diptera, including the craneflies *Cheilotrichia imbuta* and *Phalacrocera replicata*, the empid *Drapetis convergens* and the muscids *Coenosia paludis* and *Phaonia atriceps*. Magor Marsh demonstrates superbly the changes brought about by management on fenland

invertebrate faunas and the importance of conserving both grazed and ungrazed rich fens.

Nutrient-poor fens are scarce along the South Wales coast but, as mentioned earlier, pockets of sites such as Pant-y-Sais are dominated by poor-fen and small *Sphagnum* mires. The fauna of these habitats is not well-documented but an interesting association with purple moor-grass mires has been found for two rare spiders, *Glyphesis servulus* and *Baryphyma gowerense*. Prior to WPIS, *Glyphesis* was known from just a handful of English fens but has since been discovered on a number of *Molinia* mires in Wales, and *Baryphyma* was chiefly associated with upper saltmarsh habitats. Inland, nutrient-poor fens are more frequently encountered, particularly in valley bottoms, although many have been lost through drainage and agricultural improvement. In general, they are characterised by an abundance of *Molinia* tussocks and an admixture of rushes and sedges, with carpets of *Sphagnum* moss in places. Herbaceous plants frequently include meadowsweet, common valerian, angelica, sneezewort and sorrel. This is a widespread vegetation community throughout Wales and much of western Britain and as such there tend to be far fewer rarities amongst the invertebrate fauna than on the much more restricted rich fens. Here, too, species respond closely to the vegetation structure imposed by various management practices and, whilst there are common elements, there are also substantial differences between the faunas of, for instance, grazed and ungrazed fens. Burning is often carried out to provide 'spring bite' for grazing stock and there is quantitative evidence from WPIS to reinforce the intuitive conclusion that this is very detrimental to the invertebrates of poor-fen.

Examples of nutrient-poor fens can be found in each of the counties represented in South Wales Region, though they are probably commonest in West Glamorgan. Over in Gwent, Cleddon Bog is the best surviving acidic mire, consisting of a sheltered basin at 230 metres a.s.l. which supports 15 ha of unmanaged rank *Molinia* and tall heather. The most interesting species recorded so far is the money spider *Glyphesis servulus*, which appears to require rank *Molinia*. It has been recorded from Fairwood Common on Gower and at Pant-y-Sais in similar habitats. Old heather provides the breeding site for the weevil *Acalles ptinoides*, whose larvae develop inside dead stems, although this species can also utilise other types of dead wood. Also at Cleddon Bog is the scarce flea beetle *Chaetocnema confusa*, which feeds on rushes. By contrast, Cefn Gwrhyd in West Glamorgan is a mid-altitude valley mire which is grazed and periodically burnt. The more open conditions favour a greater diversity of predatory ground beetles and spiders but the fauna is chiefly composed of species which are widespread on Welsh peatlands. Among the more notable invertebrates recorded is the rare cranefly *Prionocera pubescens* which inhabits *Sphagnum* mires and is known from few British sites, having been lost from some of its localities through degradation of the habitat. Damage to such sites can be insidious, as at Nelson Bog in Mid Glamorgan where an unmanaged acidic valley mire on the Coal Measures receives run-off from the adjacent mine waste tips. The increased nutrients promote the formation of mesotrophic fen with stands of common reed and reedmace. Predictably the fauna here is more typical of the coastal rich fens with the beetles *Silis ruficollis* and *Donacia clavipes* and the hoverfly *Anasimyia contracta*. The typical invertebrates of acidic fens are more or less absent from the areas of the bog affected by the leachate, although it is at least encouraging that tall fen species have been able to colonise the site.

To return to the unmanaged nutrient-poor fens, Llannon in the Llanelli Borough of Carmarthenshire is a little-known but extensive and characteristic example of this peatland type. Although it does experience some light cattle grazing, it has not been burnt for about thirty years and this probably accounts for the presence of the *Molinia*-associated lacewing *Psectra diptera* (a curious, almost flightless, insect which is also found in tussocks of other grass species in different habitats) and the money spider *Baryphyma gowerense*. Llannon is interesting for the presence of two rare invertebrates whose status in Britain is under debate as they are thought to be comparatively recent introductions — the harvestman *Sabacon viscayanum* and the rove beetle *Hadrognathus longipalpis*. Their occurrence in such a comparatively remote site away from likely sources of introduction lends weight to the possibility that they are indeed native species. *Sabacon*, normally considered to be a woodland species, was also found by WPIS on a wet heath in Pembrokeshire and *Hadrognathus* was recorded in several peatlands in southern Wales, some of which, however, were adjacent to industrial tips. The question of origin of these species is probably impossible to resolve but on the valley mire of Llannon at least there is the possibility of investigating their roles within a typical peatland community.

Each of the peatland sites discussed above are minerotrophic, i.e. the peatland vegetation is in direct contact with groundwater from the surrounding catchment. There is only one lowland ombrotrophic mire (i.e. a peatland whose surface is supplied entirely by rainwater and hence free of the minerals and nutrients picked up from nearby soils) in the South Wales Region, at Gors Llwyn Onllwyn on the Brecknock/West Glamorgan border. Raised mires are deficient in nutrients and several studies have demonstrated that they have a naturally impoverished fauna composed of a small number of wetland generalists and raised mire specialists. These form a distinctive community which is more or less replicated on undamaged raised mires throughout western and northern Britain. Although poor in terms of numbers of species, this community is of high conservation value as it represents a natural invertebrate assemblage that is effectively unmodified by Man's activities in the British countryside and such examples of 'pure' communities are extremely rare in Britain today. It is, however, unfortunate that the section of raised mire at Gors Llwyn Onllwyn has been modified by the introduction of cattle and possibly also by interference with the peripheral hydrology. The modified nature of the mire is demonstrated by the abundance of the ant *Myrmica rubra*, which is normally found on grasslands and is generally replaced by its congeners *M. ruginodis* and *M. scabrinodis* on raised mires. Nonetheless, the ground beetles present at this site comprise an intact raised mire assemblage with *Pterostichus diligens* and *P. nigrita* (sensu lato) as dominants and the stenotopic *Agonum ericeti* also occurring. *A. ericeti*, a handsome, metallic-red carabid, can tolerate a degree of damage to its peatland habitat but as this is likely to be the only locality in the Region for this nationally uncommon beetle it would be deplorable if it became extinct here. By their very nature, unmodified raised mire faunas require their habitat to be free of all forms of interference and management and if the hydrology of the system can be restored then burning and grazing should be prevented in the future. The scarcity of this habitat type in the Region warrants intervention by conservationists to attempt to rectify some of the abuses of the past.

More information on the peatland invertebrate faunas of South Wales should be forthcoming as the results of the Welsh Peatland Invertebrate Survey are analysed and published. This large study helps us to understand some of the processes involved in maintaining the invertebrate interest of peatland habitats but we cannot pretend to have all of the answers. There is much still to be learnt about the ecological requirements of most of the peatland inhabitants and knowledge of the status and distribution of many species is still sketchy. The Region has several peatland sites of national importance for conservation and many others of Regional significance. Surveys through commissioned research and by amateur entomologists should continue in order to expand knowledge and understanding of the peatland fauna.

Uplands

Sugar Loaf, Gwent. [A.P. Fowles]

Although bordered to the north by the high peaks of Mynydd Du, Fforest Fawr, the Brecon Beacons and the Black Mountains, South Wales lacks the montane landscapes which are a component of the other Welsh Regions. The highest point, at Bal Mawr on the edge of the Black Mountains, is just 607 metres above sea level but the topography of much of the area is dominated by high ridges and steep valleys. Most of the land bounded by the Tawe in the west, the Usk in the east, and enclosed by the M4 motorway to the south, lies between 300 and 550 metres a.s.l. — a vast upland block with a distinctive character and some dramatic scenery. Industry, however, has taken its toll on the habitats of the high ground as rich seams of coal and other minerals have been extensively worked. Huge conifer forests blanket many of the plateaux between the valleys and sheep grazing on the remaining land has turned moorland into poor pasture. Whilst some good quality sites survive, it has to be admitted that the uplands do not constitute the richest habitats in the Region. This is undoubtedly a major reason for the lack

of information contained within the Invertebrate Site Register for upland sites in South Wales and only the cave system of Nant Glais on the edge of the Brecon Beacons is considered to be of national significance for invertebrate conservation. This contains several subterranean invertebrates, including the troglobitic spider *Porrhomma rosenhaueri* which is only known to occur in one other cave in Britain.

There are undoubtedly a number of fine sites remaining in the South Wales uplands but the absence of entomological data makes it impossible to assess their conservation importance for invertebrates. This is unfortunate as the history of damage makes it imperative that the best sites should be recognised at the earliest opportunity in order that the surviving upland fauna is maintained. This was highlighted by the discovery in 1972 of a moth new to Britain from moorland in Gwent at *c.* 450 metres. The Silurian *Eriopygodes imbecilla* was subsequently found to be established in reasonable numbers on the surrounding grassland. Although the female moths are active on sunny days, this species is

109

still only known from this single locality in Britain and is the most outstanding invertebrate species of the South Wales uplands. Whilst it may to some extent be overlooked on other moors it has presumably vanished from other sites in the Region through afforestation, burning or over-grazing. There is now no way of knowing how many other scarce invertebrates have declined in a similar fashion but more information is desperately required for all invertebrate orders in the uplands to conserve an adequate representation of the surviving fauna.

The twin problems of burning and over-grazing affect many of the open hills of the Region and this sadly holds true for several of the conserved sites also. In moderation both activities can be carried out without undue detriment to the upland fauna but extensive fires and high stocking levels rapidly deplete invertebrate diversity by the catastrophic changes to their habitat and the loss of food and shelter. Some of the higher hills still have populations of green hairstreak butterflies *Callophrys rubi* and graylings *Hipparchia semele* occur on abandoned mine spoil; common moths of the moors such as oak eggars *Lasiocampa quercus*, antlers *Cerapteryx graminis* and fox moths *Macrothylacia rubi* are widespread on the sheepwalks; and characteristic upland beetles, flies and spiders persist where habitats are suitable. It is, however, only where semi-natural habitats are protected from fire and over-grazing that the more interesting assemblages tend to be found. This is chiefly in bogs, pools or enclosed woodlands and surviving heather moors which are not intensively managed. Areas such as the slopes of Mynydd Llangatwg or the Black

Mountains in Gwent show promise and there is much unexplored ground on Mynydd y Glog to the west of Merthyr Tydfil. Upland lakes are scarce but the boggy fens around the corrie lakes of Craig y Llyn support the keeled skimmer dragonfly *Orthetrum coerulescens*. A typical upland cranefly fauna is present, which includes *Tipula alpium* and *Pedicia occulta*. The sheltered acidic grassland and bilberry heath below the sandstone corrie cliffs provide a refuge for montane plants and would be worth surveying for some of the scarcer upland invertebrates.

The discovery of the Silurian moth in Gwent highlights the possibilities that exist within the South Wales uplands for rewarding fieldwork with the chance of exciting finds. Although few areas are managed with the sensitivity required to maintain a rich invertebrate fauna there are sites where the incidence of burning and over-grazing is not too pronounced and these are worth searching out and surveying. In the bleak uplands, shelter in the form of moss cushions, deep heather or scattered stones, is essential to the survival of most invertebrate species at some stage in their life-cycle and sites where a representative fauna persists should be identified and managed to ensure that favourable conditions are continually present. This brief discussion reflects the lamentable lack of knowledge available on the Region's upland invertebrates but they should not be ignored as a result of historical neglect. Survey effort should be directed towards suitable habitats and protected sites, such as the heather moors of Blorenge, should be managed more sympathetically to conserve a full spectrum of upland wildlife.

Acknowledgements

The Invertebrate Site Register (ISR) has developed as a team effort since its inception and this review of Wales has only been possible through the commitment and motivation of many individuals. Most of the information was initially collated by Dr Jennifer Rees in 1983 and subsequently by contract staff working for the Nature Conservancy Council's Terrestrial Invertebrate Zoology Branch. The development of the ISR has arisen chiefly from the determination and enthusiasm of Alan Stubbs and Dr Ian McLean and invertebrate conservation owes a great deal to their efforts and knowledge. My colleagues on the ISR have helped tremendously at all stages of the production of the review. Now under the auspices of the Species Conservation Branch of the Joint Nature Conservation Committee, the ISR is the direct responsibility of Dr Stuart Ball and Margaret Palmer, whose support has been invaluable during the latter stages of this project.

I would like to thank all of the above for their encouragement and advice. I would also like to acknowledge the assistance, for which I am extremely grateful, of the following: Dr Keith Alexander, Dave Boyce, Arthur Chater, Dr Ian Francis, Dr Peter Holmes, Tony Irwin, Dr Roger Key, Derek Lott, Ian Morgan and Joan Morgan. Valuable comments on the relevant Regional sections were provided at draft stage by the District Officers of the Countryside Council for Wales. The production of this review has benefitted considerably during the pre-publication stages from the commitment and advice of John Bratton and Roger Morris.

The Countryside Council for Wales and the Joint Nature Conservation Committee are grateful to the following for contributing information on sites and species in Wales to the Invertebrate Site Register:

Dr K.N.A. Alexander, D.J.L. Agassiz, I. Bowen, D.C. Boyce, J.H. Bratton, Dr R.P. Bray, A. Brennan, J.M. Brummit, J.T. Burn, K.M. Catley, A.O. Chater, Dr J. Chatfield, Dr M. Claridge, D.K. Clements, L.T. Colley, S.J. Coker, P.S. Cranston, J. Deeming, Dr J.M. Eddington, D.A. Edwards, Lt. Col. A.M. Emmet, S.B. Evans, T.G. Evans, S.J. Falk, I. Fawthrop, A.C. Fegan, A.P. Fowles, Dr A.D. Fox, N.E. Gammon, Dr M.E. Gillham, R. Goodier, A. Graham, S.J. Grove, J. Hall, R.J. Haycock, D.G. Holland, Dr G.A.N. Horton, M.J. Hubbard, M.R. Hughes, M.S. Ilett, G.T. Jefferson, R.A. Jenkins, C. Johnson, C.A. Jones, W. Keen, Dr R.S. Key, Dr P. Kirby, S.J.J. Lambert, V. Lorimer, Dr N. Lowe, Dr R.G. Loxton, Dr I.F.G. McLean, R.W. Martin, C. Merrett, II.N. Michaelis, I.K. Morgan, M.J. Morgan, W. Nelson, Dr C. O'Toole, Prof. J.A. Owen, M. Palmer, M.S. Parsons, C.R.C. Paul, P.M. Pavett, I. Perry, S. Pooles, P.A. Rowlings, C.A. Scurr, Dr A.N.B. Simpson, P. Skidmore, B.W. Staddon, K. Stevens, A.E. Stubbs, R.D. Sutton, I. Thomas, C. Titcombe, A. Vaughan Jones, Dr I.D. Wallace, Dr D.A. Wells, I. White, Dr I.M. White and E.N. Willmer.

Photographic credits

S.G. Ball — facing page 16, 22, 37, facing page 48, 56, 61, facing page 112; R.P. Bray — 7, 11, 67, 78, facing page 97; A.O. Chater — facing page 33, facing page 64, facing page 129; A.P. Fowles — cover, facing page 16, facing page 17, 18, 21, 26, facing page 32, facing page 33, 34, facing page 48, 48, facing page 49, 54, 59, 63, facing page 64, facing page 65, 69, facing page 80, facing page 81, 83, 95, facing page 96, 97, 99, 104, 109, facing page 112, facing page 113, facing page 128, facing page 129; M. Hammett — cover, facing page 128; P. Hope Jones — 15; S. Hopkin — 50; D.G. Jones — 45; R.S. Key — cover, 33, 65, facing page 80, 80, 89, 93, 102, 106, facing page 129; M.E.N. Majerus — facing page 81; Nature Conservancy Council — 40, 91, facing page 97, facing page 129; J. Porter — 28, 43, facing page 48, facing page 97, facing page 128; Prema Photos — facing page 32, facing page 64; D.G. Rands — facing page 17, facing page 33; J.B. Ratcliffe — 87, facing page 112; I.J.L. Tillotson — 73; P. Wakely — 30, facing page 33; I.D. Wallace — facing page 113; P. Waring — cover, facing page 49, facing page 65, 75, facing page 97.

Notable sites for the conservation of invertebrates in Wales (see Appendix 1.)

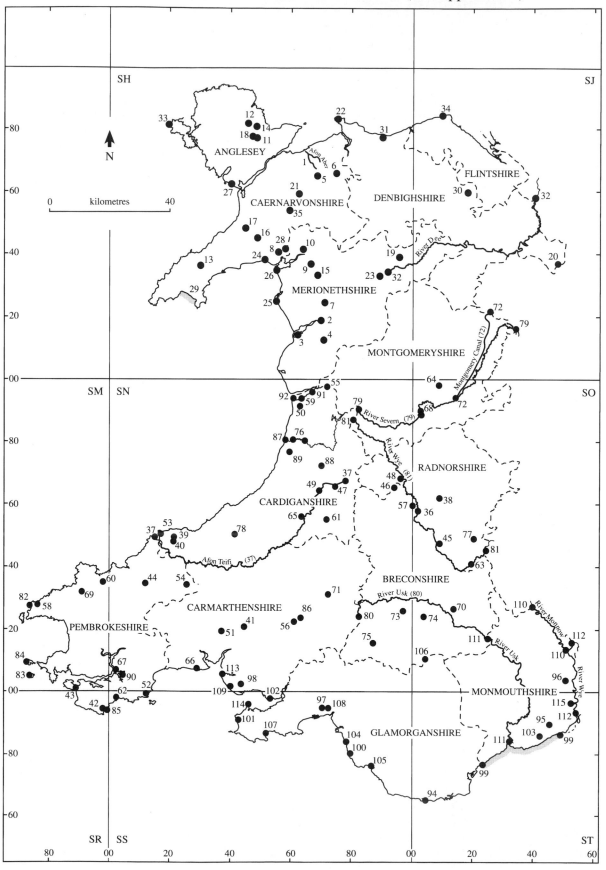

Cors Goch, Anglesey: The rich valley fens of North Wales are amongst the best of their kind in Britain and are valuable habitats for peatland invertebrates.
(Photograph by J.B. Ratcliffe.)

Stratiomys chamaeleon **(Diptera):** Many soldier flies have semi-aquatic larvae that develop in unpolluted, shallow flushes and hence they are useful as indicators of habitat quality. *S. chamaeleon* is a rare species of base-rich flushes which occurs on several of Anglesey's rich fens.
(Photograph by S.G. Ball.)

Llangloffan Fen, Dyfed: Light grazing on the valley fens creates a mosaic of tussocks and shorter vegetation. This is ideal habitat for many peatland ground beetles and other invertebrate predators as they can hunt over the more open ground and shelter amongst the litter layer at the base of the tussocks.
(Photograph by A.P. Fowles.)

Magor Marsh, Gwent: Ungrazed fens are valuable for invertebrates that require a continuous layer of dense litter or that breed in and amongst the stems of tall fenland plants. Magor Marsh is the only substantial area of fenland remaining on the Gwent Levels.
(Photograph by A.P. Fowles.)

Hagenella clathrata **(Trichoptera):** Inhabiting tussocky grassland at the edge of lowland raised mires, this attractive diurnal caddisfly only just occurs in Wales, at Bettisfield Moss in Denbighshire. (Photograph by I.D. Wallace.)

Crymlyn Bog, West Glamorgan: The largest area of lowland fen in Wales and a nationally important peatland site with an exceptional invertebrate fauna.
(Photograph by A.P. Fowles.)

Appendix 1

Notable sites for the conservation of invertebrates in Wales

The following lists describe those sites in Wales for which current information indicates that the localities are of notable significance for the range and quality of their invertebrate faunas. Despite the tradition of entomological recording in parts of the country it is inevitable that this list must be regarded as incomplete. There is scope for further surveys to be carried out on all of the sites listed and there are certainly many sites with good invertebrate habitat that have the potential to be added to this list when more is known about their resident faunas.

The inclusion of a site on this list does not imply that there is open access. In the case of nature reserves, the relevant conservation organisation should be contacted with details of survey proposals. In these cases access will normally be granted, although some restrictions may be imposed to take account of other aspects of reserve management. Many of the other sites listed are notified as Sites of Special Scientific Interest and permission, in the first instance, should be sought from the relevant District Officer of the Countryside Council for Wales who will be able to advise on the correct procedures for access. In all cases the permission of the landowner must be granted before surveys are carried out. The addresses of organisations with an interest in the conservation of invertebrates in the Wales are to be found in Appendix 2.

North Wales

1. **Afon Aber** (SH688674 to SH662718 and SH698699 to SH662718) — The Afon Rhaeadr-fawr and Afon Anafon are two upland branches of the Afon Aber which drain the northern slopes of the Carneddau. They are precipitous, stony streams containing a typical upland aquatic invertebrate fauna which is characteristically dominated by stoneflies, including the relatively scarce species *Capnia vidua*, *Protonemura montana* and *Amphinemura standfussi*. The Afon Rhaeadr-fawr is partly contained within Coedydd Aber National Nature Reserve.

2. **Afon Mawddach** (SH71-19-) — At the upper limit of tidal influence, above the confluence of the Afon Wnion, the Mawddach deposits shoals of mixed gravels on its banks. These support a good range of invertebrates which are specialised inhabitants of river shingle, particularly beetles and spiders, several of which are regarded as nationally rare.

3. **Arthog Bog** (SH634145) — Although affected by agricultural reclamation and drainage, the estuarine raised mire of Arthog Bog still has a central core which is largely intact. A characteristic lowland acidic peatland fauna is present along with a number of nationally scarce species amongst a range of invertebrate orders.

4. **Cadair Idris** (SH72-13-) — At 893 metres, this is the southernmost high peak of the Snowdonia mountains and its montane habitats support a limited number of high altitude specialists such as the spider *Micaria alpina* and the ground beetle *Leistus montanus*. The lower slopes of the Cadair Idris ridge contain a range of small mires, unimproved grasslands and relict woodlands of considerable invertebrate interest, including a colony of the marsh fritillary *Eurodryas aurinia*, a scarce species in North Wales. The majority of Cadair Idris is a National Nature Reserve and part is owned by the National Trust.

5. **Carneddau** (SH70-65-) — The largest and most remote upland block in Snowdonia, which is not as well known entomologically as some of the more popular areas but has considerable potential for montane invertebrates. Upland beetles include *Leistus montanus* and *Oxypoda tirolensis* and the spiders *Tiso aestivus* and *Meioneta nigripes* have also been recorded. Several scarce alpine sawflies are present and the aquatic fauna of streams and lakes also has interesting upland elements. The National Trust owns a large area of the Carneddau.

6. **Coed Dolgarrog** (SH766657) — This National Nature Reserve is a block of lowland deciduous woodland on the western slopes of the Vale of Conwy. The rich ground flora promotes a good phytophagous fauna and surveys of Lepidoptera and Coleoptera have revealed a number of scarce species in both groups. Further recording is desirable.

7. **Coed Ganllwyd** (SH723243) — A valley oakwood consisting of neglected coppice on steep, east-facing slopes above the Afon Mawddach. The wood is humid with an abundance of bryophytes and ferns and is important chiefly for Diptera associated with streambanks and shaded woodlands. Owned by the National Trust and managed as a National Nature Reserve.

8. **Coed Tremadog** (SH569405) — An oak-ash-hazel woodland on the unstable cliffs above the floodplain of the Afon Glaslyn. Areas of open cliff and blocky scree add diversity to the habitats present. This National Nature Reserve has received little attention entomologically because of the dangerous nature of the terrain, although a survey in 1975 demonstrated that this is an important site for woodland Diptera.

9. **Coed y Rhygen** (SH680369) — Birch and sessile oak dominate this upland woodland on the steep banks of Llyn Trawsfynydd. Small heathy glades and mires are scattered throughout. There is little information available on this National Nature Reserve apart from surveys of the butterflies and the Diptera. However, the latter have been extensively recorded and many interesting and scarce species are present, including the rare cranefly *Triogma trisulcata*.

10. **Coedydd Maentwrog** (SH652415) — An extensive block of sessile oakwoods on the south-facing slopes of the Vale of Ffestiniog. The scarce arboreal ground beetle *Calosoma inquisitor* has been recorded and the woodland dipteran fauna contains a range of uncommon species. There would appear to be plenty of scope for further profitable recording in this National Nature Reserve.

114

11. **Cors Bodeilio** (SH497772) — A calcareous valley mire in the Malltraeth Trough on Anglesey with a range of fen and wet meadow habitats. This is a rich and important site for lowland fen invertebrates and many scarce species have been recorded, including the leaf hopper *Cicadella lasiocarpae* which is otherwise only known from the nearby mires of Cors Erddreiniog (q.v.) and Cors Geirch (q.v.) on Lleyn. Part of Cors Bodeilio is a National Nature Reserve.

12. **Cors Erddreiniog** (SH470820) — The three fen basins of this large calcareous valley mire contain a diverse mixture of wetland habitats demonstrating a variety of management practices. The invertebrate fauna is outstanding and many national rarities have been recorded, including the soldier fly *Stratiomys chamaeleon*, the southern damselfly *Coenagrion mercuriale* and the leaf hopper *Cicadella lasiocarpae*. Part of Cors Erddreiniog is a National Nature Reserve.

13. **Cors Geirch** (SH315363) — The calcareous valley mire of Cors Geirch extends for five kilometres and is the best example of the habitat-type in North Wales outside Anglesey. Entomologically it is regarded as one of the best wetland sites on the mainland in North Wales and many rare species have been recorded. Part of Cors Geirch is a National Nature Reserve.

14. **Cors Goch** (SH497813) — Another of the Anglesey valley mires, containing calcareous fen influenced by the Carboniferous Limestone which surrounds and crosses the valley. The western basin includes a small lake, Llyn Cadarn, which has an interesting water beetle fauna. Cors Goch shares many of the interesting fenland species recorded from Cors Bodeilio and Cors Erddreiniog. Most of the mire is managed as a nature reserve by the North Wales Wildlife Trust.

15. **Cors Goch Trawsfynydd** (SH699334) — A raised mire and associated poor-fen habitats situated in a broad shallow valley to the south of Llyn Trawsfynydd. The large heath butterfly *Coenonympha tullia* is well established here and, despite past peat-cutting activities, the ombrotopic ground beetle *Agonum ericeti* is common. This large site has received comparatively little entomological attention and would repay further investigations.

16. **Cors Graianog** (SH497454) — An acidic basin mire at 170 metres a.s.l. on the boundary between the Lleyn Peninsula and Snowdonia. The invertebrate fauna reflects the ombrogenous nature of the site and offers an interesting contrast with the rich fens of Lleyn.

17. **Cors Gyfelog** (SH459482) — A large area of wetland habitats at the head of the Afon Dwyfach on the Lleyn Peninsula. There is a mixture of acidic and poor-fen mire communities interspersed with small pools and willow carr. A rich invertebrate fauna is present which includes a strong population of the rare weevil *Bagous frit*. Part of the site is managed as a National Nature Reserve.

18. **Cors y Farl** (SH490779) — An important site for water beetles with a rich assemblage of species associated with the partially-drained lake which occupies most of this calcareous valley mire. The surrounding fen is also of interest for wetland invertebrates.

19. **Cors-y-sarnau** (SH970388) — A shallow valley fen largely dominated by alder and willow carr but also containing pockets of open seepage fen. The Diptera associated with the carr and flushes include several scarce wetland species. Cors-y-sarnau is of particular significance as a geographically isolated example of the entomologically rich valley fens in the Region. Managed as a nature reserve by the North Wales Wildlife Trust.

20. **Fenn's Moss** (SJ489369) — The 680 ha complex of Fenn's, Whixall and Bettisfield Mosses comprises one of the largest areas of lowland raised mire in England and Wales. The site straddles the boundary of Clwyd and Shropshire and is perhaps best known to entomologists as "Whixall Moss". The largest area, Fenn's Moss, is situated in Clwyd and consists of a mixture of intact raised mire, old peat-cuttings, and commercially-worked peat with many bog pools and invasive birch scrub. The site has been historically well-studied and contains an exceptional fauna with many national rarities, although modern confirmation is required for some of the less conspicuous species in light of the recent damage caused by commercial peat extraction. The area has now become a National Nature Reserve and management will aim to raise the water table and restore bog vegetation to the damaged peat.

21. **Glydeiriau** (SH640590) — Owned by the National Trust, this area of montane heath and grassland surrounds and includes the National Nature Reserve of Cwm Idwal. The site encompasses the northern slopes of Glyder Fawr (999 metres a.s.l.) and Glyder Fach (994 metres)

and their corrie lakes. Upland invertebrates recorded include the nationally scarce spider *Micaria alpina* and the rove beetle *Ocyusa hibernica*.

22. **Great Orme's Head** (SH767833) — A spectacular outcrop of Carboniferous Limestone at the east end of Conwy Bay. The summit is sheep-grazed but the steeper slopes are a mixture of scrub and stony grassland maintained by feral goats. This is a nationally important site for Lepidoptera with endemic dwarf sub-species of the silver-studded blue *Plebejus argus caernensis* and the grayling *Hipparchia semele thyone* and several nationally scarce species of moths. Other invertebrate groups are less well-known but there is an interesting phytophagous beetle fauna and further studies would be valuable. Most of the area of biological interest is managed as a Local Nature Reserve by Aberconwy Borough Council and there is a North Wales Wildlife Trust reserve on the south-west facing cliffs.

23. **Llyn Tegid** (SH905330) — Llyn Tegid (also known as Bala Lake) is the largest natural lake in Wales, extending for six kilometres and reaching a depth of 42 metres in a glacially-cut basin along a geological fault line. The aquatic invertebrate fauna is generally typical of oligotrophic-mesotrophic lakes but there has been a deterioration of quality since the lake became a reservoir in 1955. A few years before this the very rare glutinous snail *Myxas glutinosa* was recorded for the last time in Llyn Tegid but it may still occur.

24. **Llyn Ystumllyn** (SH526385) — A coastal fen which has developed on the site of a former shallow lake which was drained in the 1950s. Reedswamp, fen meadow and carr are the main wetland habitats present and the site supports a diverse range of characteristic and uncommon invertebrates.

25. **Morfa Dyffryn** (SH555250) — A large dune system on the Meirionnydd coast between Barmouth and Harlech, with well-developed slacks, and a sheltered saltmarsh in the lee of Shell Island. Rather neglected entomologically but available information suggests that Morfa Dyffryn has a typically rich and important dune invertebrate fauna. Most of the site lies within the Morfa Dyffryn National Nature Reserve.

26. **Morfa Harlech** (SH560350) — The National Nature Reserve of Morfa Harlech extends for approximately four kilometres along the coast on the south side of the Glaslyn estuary. There are good fore dune habitats at the northern tip but the reserve is mainly of importance for its extensive dune slacks and tracts of dune pasture. An interesting transition zone occurs alongside the saltmarsh of Traeth Bach. Important invertebrate assemblages are present throughout the dune system and this is a locality of national significance for groups such as the Diptera, Coleoptera and aculeate Hymenoptera.

27. **Newborough Warren** (SH425365) — One of the largest dune systems in Britain and correspondingly regarded as a nationally important site for a wide range of invertebrate groups. This National Nature Reserve has received considerable entomological attention and an extensive list of uncommon species has been recorded. The island of Ynys Llanddwyn at the western end of the reserve provides additional habitats of interest and is important for its populations of bees and wasps. Adjacent to the NNR, the conifer plantation of Newborough Forest has broad sandy rides which are also significant for invertebrate conservation and the medicinal leech *Hirudo medicinalis* is known from at least one pool in the forest.

28. **Pont Croesor** (SH593415) — An area of floodplain fen on the banks of the Afon Glaslyn, consisting chiefly of fen meadow but also containing valuable riverside carr woodland. A rich wetland invertebrate fauna has been recorded and this is one of few Welsh sites for the rare whorl snail *Vertigo lilljeborgi*.

29. **Porth Neigwl** (SH242283 — SH290255) — South-west facing soft-rock cliffs stretching for six kilometres at the tip of the Lleyn Peninsula. This is the most extensive example of this habitat type in Wales. The cliffs are largely unstable but there are also sections of semi-stable grassland and shallow flushes. Only the Coleoptera have been well-worked but the presence of species such as the ground beetle *Tachys micros* and the psephenid *Eubria palustris* indicate the importance of Porth Neigwl for invertebrate conservation.

30. **Pothole Valley** (SJ191598) — A mosaic of deciduous woodland and unimproved grassland on the slopes of the Carboniferous Limestone outcrop of Bryn Alun. Sheltered edge habitats support a rich insect fauna and calcareous streams rising from springs on the lower slopes add further diversity. The rare myrmecophilous beetle *Amauronyx maerkeli* has been recorded and

the phytophagous and saproxylic Coleoptera include several scarce species.

31. **Rhyd-y-foel** (SH915775) — Steep west-facing slopes of the Afon Dulas, supporting scrub woodland and limestone grassland. A rich lepidopteran fauna is present, including a long-established introduced population of the dwarf form of the silver-studded blue *Plebejus argus caernensis*. This is one of few Welsh localities for the scarce plume moth *Pterophorus spilodactylus* and the cistus forester *Adscita geryon* occurs in small numbers. There is no information available on other invertebrate orders and surveys would be very interesting.

32. **River Dee** (SH929351 — SJ407584) — Emerging from Llyn Tegid (q.v.), the River Dee flows eastwards to the English border before heading north to leave Wales south of Chester. For much of its length it is stony-bedded and fast-flowing but beyond the Vale of Llangollen the river is deep and meandering with a silty bed. The freshwater invertebrates have been well-studied and there is a diverse fauna of stoneflies, mayflies and caddisflies, reflecting the fact that water quality in the upper reaches is generally good. A speciality of the Dee is the large stonefly *Isogenus nubecula* which is not known with certainty from any other British river. The Dee has a good range of bankside habitats but the terrestrial and semi-aquatic invertebrate faunas are neglected and would benefit from survey.

33. **South Stack** (SH210824) — An extensive tract of coastal heathland at the tip of Holy Island. The silver-studded blue *Plebejus argus* is widespread here in its largest heathland colony in Wales. The scarce chafer *Amphimallon ochraceus* has been recorded but generally there is little information on other invertebrates present. South Stack is a reserve of the Royal Society for the Protection of Birds.

34. **Talacre Warren** (SJ110850) — The five kilometre stretch between Prestatyn and the Point of Ayr is the only substantial dune system surviving on the north coast of Wales. Despite public pressure there is still considerable invertebrate interest on Talacre Warren and, in particular, there is a good representative sand dune moth fauna. The sandhill rustic *Luperina nickerlii gueneei* occurs here at one of its few British sites and there are also nationally scarce moths associated with the rich dune slacks, fore dunes and saltmarsh.

35. **Yr Wyddfa** (SH609543) — At 1085 metres a.s.l. the summit of Snowdon (Yr Wyddfa) is the highest mountain in England and Wales. This vast block, part of which is managed as a National Nature Reserve, contains montane grassland, corrie lakes, crags and screes. The speciality, of course, is the 'Snowdon beetle', *Chrysolina cerealis*, but there is also a good range of other nationally restricted montane invertebrates, particularly amongst the beetles and spiders.

Dyfed-Powys

36. Aberithon Turbary (SO015574) — A former turbary occupying a periglacial depression which has areas of reedswamp, willow carr and acidic fen. The site contains a characteristic water beetle community of relict basin fens and there is also a good range of phytophagous beetles associated with the rich marsh flora. Wetland Diptera are also well-represented, including the rare cranefly *Prionocera pubescens*. The site is managed as a nature reserve by the Radnor Wildlife Trust.

37. Afon Teifi (SN7867 — SN1549) — A nationally important river system with a particularly rich mayfly and caddisfly fauna, including *Baetis digitatus*, *B. atrebatinus*, *Oecetis notata*, *Ylodes simulans* and *Lasiocephala basalis*. The lower reaches are of regional importance for the banded demoiselle *Calopteryx splendens*.

38. Bailey Einon (SO083615) — Base-rich valleyside woodland with floodplain alder carr on the banks of the River Ithon. The mixed canopy and species-rich shrub layer contribute to the diversity of the woodland invertebrate fauna and open glades provide valuable nectar sources for insects. The scarce riverbank click beetle *Selatosomus angustulus* (a Powys speciality) is present along with many uncommon dead wood beetles, including *Schizotus pectinicornis* and *Pyrrhidium sanguineum*. The adjacent shingle banks and earth cliffs lining the River Ithon add to the habitat diversity of the site. Owned by Radnor Wildlife Trust.

39. Banc-y-mwldan (SN201489) — Unimproved neutral grassland with an extensive series of soligenous flushes which are base-enriched from adjacent deposits of glacial drift. Fen and mire communities associated with the flushes support a rich wetland fauna including a number of uncommon soldier flies, most notably a strong population of *Odontomyia hydroleon*.

40. Banc-y-warren (SN201484) — Active quarry in the glacial sands lying adjacent to Banc-y-mwldan with patches of open, firm sand, vertical cliff-faces, ruderal vegetation and shallow pools. This site is of considerable potential for the distinctive assemblage of invertebrates associated with such habitats and the known presence of the scarce ground beetle *Amara fulva* is indicative of the value of Banc-y-warren for psammophilous invertebrates.

41. Bishop's Pond, Abergwili (SN445210) — The best example of an ox-bow lake in West Wales and of particular importance for its broad fen of reed sweet-grass. The open water supports at least fourteen species of dragonfly, including the hairy dragonfly *Brachytron pratense*, and the fluctuating water table provides a fringe of bare mud during the summer which is favoured by a range of Diptera species.

42. Bosherston Lake (Stackpole NNR) (SR975945) — A coastal marl lake formed by the damming of three narrow valleys in the Carboniferous Limestone during the mid 19th century. The shallow, calcareous waters support rich submerged macrophyte communities and, in places where the banks are shallow, there are patches of reedswamp with a diverse marsh flora. The lake is especially important for its caddisfly fauna, with such species as *Ecnomus tenellus*, *Orthotrichia costalis* and *Leptocerus tineiformis*. Owned by the National Trust.

43. Broomhill Burrows (SM890004) — Part owned by the National Trust, this is one of the largest dune systems in Pembrokeshire and is especially notable for the diversity of its dune slacks. The dune fauna includes a good range of scarce species from many invertebrate orders. A notable feature of the low cliffs at the southern end of the bay is the abundance and variety of seepages which support many rare flies including *Dolichopus signifer*.

44. Brynberian Moor (SN115345) — An extensive mosaic of wet lowland heath and moorland on the northern slopes of Mynydd Preseli, heavily grazed by sheep and ponies. The area is dissected throughout by numerous flushes, streams and springs and small basin fens are also present. Brynberian is a nationally important locality for dragonflies and supports the largest British colony of *Coenagrion mercuriale* outside the New Forest.

45. Coed Aberedw (SO083471) — A north-facing sessile oakwood on rocky slopes above the Afon Edw, containing maiden trees and ancient coppice. The ground flora is generally poor on the dry and acidic shaley substrate but there are several calcareous flushes which introduce floristic diversity to the ground layer. A good range of invertebrates indicative of ancient woodland has been recorded but Coed Aberedw is of especial interest for the presence of the rare pill woodlouse *Armadillidium pictum*, which is known from only a handful of sites in Britain. The adjacent grassy slopes of Aberedw Rocks, interspersed with scree and crags, are also of interest.

46. **Coed Cnwch/Allt Ddu** (SN935649) — A west-facing block of ancient sessile oakwood on the slopes of the Elan Valley. The wood is sheep-grazed and the boulder-strewn floor is carpeted by mosses with locally dominant patches of bilberry. Many of the trees are of great age and provide a variety of saproxylic habitats for invertebrates, amongst which the beetles have been recently surveyed.

47. **Coed Mynachlog-fawr** (SN744653) — A large area of ancient neglected sessile oak coppice which has been historically grazed and represents an important example of pasture-woodland with an unimproved acidic ground flora containing numerous flushes and small mires. The interesting mosaic of habitats is of great value to invertebrates and species recorded include the beetles *Dendroxena quadrimaculata* and *Abdera flexuosa*, and the cone-headed fly *Conops vesicularis*.

48. **Coed-y-cefn** (SN955677) — This sessile oakwood is of great ecological interest for its extraordinary abundance of nest mounds of the wood ant *Formica lugubris*, which is particularly remarkable as the wood marks the southern limit of this species in Britain. The ants have a profound influence on the woodland eco-system and are also host to a number of scarce myrmecophilous invertebrates, including the leaf beetle *Clytra quadripunctata* whose larvae develop inside the ants' nests.

49. **Cors Caron NNR** (SN690640) — A complex of three raised mires, disected by the Afon Teifi and its tributaries, and displaying a full sequence of habitats from river-terraces and carr to the hummock-hollow communities of the central domes. The peatland fauna has been the subject of several investigations and includes the most southerly British colony of the large heath butterfly *Coenonympha tullia*, along with many other nationally scarce species of Lepidoptera, and one of two known Welsh colonies of the spider *Singa hamata*.

50. **Cors Fochno, Dyfi NNR** (SN630910) — An estuarine raised mire, one of the largest tracts of unmodified, actively-growing, raised bog in Britain. The rosy marsh moth *Eugraphe subrosea*

has its major British stronghold here and the bog bush cricket *Metrioptera brachyptera* (a scarce species in Wales) is well-established. A wide range of noteworthy peatland invertebrates has been recorded and the dragonfly fauna of old peat-cuttings is of national significance.

51. **Cors Goch, Llanllwch** (SN365188) — Cors Goch, the southernmost raised mire in Britain, is situated in a shallow valley to the west of Carmarthen. The vegetation communities are typical of such bog habitats and the central dome also contains numerous steep-sided pools. There has been little invertebrate recording undertaken to date but the presence of species such as the bog bush cricket *Metrioptera brachyptera* and the small red damselfly *Ceriagrion tenellum* in their only known localities in Carmarthenshire suggest the likely occurrence of other scarce species. Part of the site is owned by the Dyfed Wildlife Trust.

52. **Cors Penally** (SS118989) — A diverse area of coastal rich fen with an exceptional flora reflecting the calcareous influences of adjacent limestone and sand dunes. Recent survey has revealed the presence of an equally diverse invertebrate fauna which includes a number of scarce beetles and flies, typified by the presence of uncommon wetland ground beetles such as *Elaphrus uliginosus*, *Chlaenius nigricornis* and *Oodes helopioides*. Most of the site is owned by the Ministry of Defence.

53. **Creigiau Gwbert** (SN160500) — A two kilometre stretch of coastal cliff at the mouth of the Afon Teifi, with sections of flushed boulder-clay and hard-rock cliff topped by unimproved coastal grassland. The rare cranefly *Gonomyia bradleyi* has been found on the flushes here and other notable coastal species include the chafer *Amphimallon ochraceus* and the water beetle *Ochthebius subinteger*.

54. **Cwm Gwaun** (SN025340) — The Gwaun Valley woodlands extend for more than five kilometres and are composed chiefly of neglected oak coppice with a hazel understorey and localised blocks of ash-wych elm woodland. The valley bottom contains numerous unimproved damp pastures with a herb-rich flora and the site is a good example of a woodland mosaic which provides substantial edge-habitat of value for invertebrates. There has been little systematic recording carried out although the variety of Lepidoptera reported, including such species as the scarce burnished brass *Diachrysia chryson*, clouded magpie *Abraxas sylvata* and cloaked

carpet *Euphyia biangulata*, indicate the site's potential.

55. **Cwm Llyfnant** (SN720973) — North-facing slopes of the Afon Llyfnant valley, containing a mosaic of ancient woodland and flushed moorland. The uncommon longhorn beetle *Judolia cerambyciformis* is abundant here and small fens in the valley bottom support a number of scarce flies, including the hoverfly *Eristalis rupium*. The site is owned by the Royal Society for the Protection of Birds.

56. **Dinefwr Deer Park** (SN610225) — Recent survey has shown Dinefwr to be amongst the top national sites for the conservation of dead wood Coleoptera with *Platypus cylindrus*, *Xyleborus dryographus* and *Thymalus limbatus* amongst the twenty-three saproxylic habitat indicators so far recorded. The abundance of dead and dying timber associated with the huge oaks in a pasture-woodland setting are also important for Diptera, including the rare hoverfly *Callicera aenea*, and Dinefwr is probably the best dead wood site for invertebrates in south Wales. Owned by the National Trust.

57. **Doldowlodd & Llysdinam Estates** (SN99-59- & SO009582) — These adjacent parklands contain a high proportion of large old oak trees which support a number of nationally scarce saproxylic beetles, including the Powys specialities *Schizotus pectinicornis* and *Pyrrhidium sanguineum*. Only the beetles have been adequately surveyed to date and further invertebrate recording is desirable.

58. **Dowrog Common** (SM775273) — More than 100 hectares of wet heathland and valley fen mosaic with associated pools and grasslands. All of the site is common land owned by the National Trust and managed by the Dyfed Wildlife Trust. Dowrog Common contains a large colony of *Ceriagrion tenellum* along with other characteristic wet heathland dragonflies. The site is also of significance for wetland Diptera, including the scarce sciomyzids *Colobaea bifasciella* and *C. distincta*.

59. **Dyfi Saltmarsh** (SN635936) — Much of the Dyfi estuary is dominated by cord-grass but there are still extensive pockets of upper saltmarsh with a red fescue sward. Characteristic ground beetles such as *Bembidion laterale*, *B. minimum* and *B. iricolor* are present and the scarce scarabaeid *Aphodius plagiatus* is frequent amongst strandline debris. Included within Dyfi NNR.

60. **Esgyrn Bottom** (SM976347) — The most south-westerly raised mire in Britain, occupying the floor of a subglacial meltwater channel. Parts of the central dome still retain an uneven surface of hummocks and hollows but past drainage and peat-cutting has affected the hydrology of most of the bog. Little invertebrate recording has taken place to date but the rare money spider *Glyphesis servulus* is present and marsh fritillaries *Eurodryas aurinia* breed on the fringe.

61. **Figyn Blaen-brefi** (SN717547) — Forty hectares of watershed mire and peat-hags in the south-eastern uplands of Cardiganshire, owned by the Forestry Commission and leased to the Dyfed Wildlife Trust. The site has a characteristic blanket mire fauna which includes the ground beetle *Agonum ericeti* and the rare caddisfly *Oxyethira mirabilis*.

62. **Freshwater East** (SS023982) — South-facing cliffs and head deposits adjacent to the small sand dune system at Freshwater East with a variety of seepages over hard rock, clay and gravels. A rich dipteran fauna is associated with these seepages, including nationally scarce species such as *Limonia goritiensis*, *Gonomyia conoviensis*, *Clinocera nigra* and *Hercostomus chetifer*.

63. **Glasbury Shingle Beds** (SO184405) — An extensive stretch of river shingle on the north bank of the River Wye, including backwaters and mature willow carr. The river bank deposits are partially vegetated and composed of a mixture of sand and pebbles. The site has been well-worked for beetles and many rare shingle inhabitants, such as *Thalassophilus longicornis* and *Negastrius sabulicola*, have been recorded. Further survey is required on other invertebrate groups but the nationally rare empid *Tachydromia acklandi* is already known to occur here.

64. **Gregynog Great Wood** (SO082976) — A large block of ancient pasture-woodland dominated by oak standards above sheep-grazed acidic grassland. The wood is under-worked entomologically, in common with so much of Montgomeryshire, but the stature of the trees and the abundance of dead wood habitats indicates its potential. To date, only a handful of saproxylic habitat indicator species have been recorded, such as *Thymalus limbatus*, *Ctesias serra*, *Pediacus dermestoides* and *Stenichnus bicolor*, but it is likely that the site will prove to be of Regional importance when further surveys have been carried out. Owned by the University of Wales.

120

65. Gwaun Garthenor a Llanio-isaf
(SN635557) — Poor-fen and substantial amounts
of well-developed alder and willow carr border a
floodplain mire on the banks of the Afon Teifi.
The floodplain contains a large population of the
relict snail *Vertigo lilljeborgi* and the nationally
rare water beetle *Hydroporus rufifrons* has been
recently recorded. Several uncommon wetland
flies are present, including the hoverfly *Microdon
mutabilis* and the sciomyzids *Pherbellia dorsata* and
Euthycera fumigata. Part of the site is owned by
the Woodland Trust.

66. Laugharne Burrows (SN290075) — This
sand dune system, owned by the Ministry of
Defence, is the largest in West Wales and is
especially notable for its extensive dune slacks.
Restricted access has limited survey opportunities
but this is clearly an important site for duneland
invertebrates and for species found in calcium-
rich waters, provided for here by Witchett Pool.

67. Lawrenny Wood (SN013075) — Thirty-six
hectares of mature hanging oakwood on the east
bank of the Daugleddau estuary, part-owned by
the National Trust. Sections of this ancient
woodland contain massive trees which support
an important dead wood fauna of Regional
importance. Further survey is desirable but the
presence of species such as *Pediacus dermestoides*,
Rhizophagus nitidulus, *Dorcatoma chrysomelina* and
Malthodes guttifer suggest that Lawrenny Wood is
one of the best ancient woodlands for
invertebrates in Dyfed.

68. Llandinam Shingle Banks (SO023877 —
SO025897) — Although the River Severn has
not been comprehensively surveyed for the
invertebrate fauna of its shingle banks, it is
evident that this section is of high quality with
regard to structure and extent. Recent survey has
provided evidence of this with several nationally
scarce shingle beetles having been recorded,
including *Perileptus areolatus*, *Lathrobium
angusticolle*, *Aloconota eichhoffi* and *Meotica anglica*.

69. Llangloffan Fen NNR (SM905318) — An
extensive valley fen on the banks of the Western
Cleddau, containing much common reed but also
including stands of greater tussock-sedge and
great fen-sedge. A characteristic fauna of
ungrazed tall-fen vegetation is present, with a
good range of nationally scarce species having
been recorded.

70. Llangorse Lake (SO133265) — A large
(200 hectare), shallow, eutrophic lake occupying
a kettle-hole in Old Red Sandstone drift — the
largest natural water-body in South Wales. The
aquatic and marginal vegetation is particularly
rich although the site has suffered from a variety
of problems arising from pollution and recreation
pressure. Deterioration of the macro-invertebrate
community may have resulted from these
damaging activities and there is a need for
present-day information on the invertebrate
fauna. A rich molluscan fauna has been
recorded, including several species which are
locally distributed in Wales, and the medicinal
leech *Hirudo medicinalis* has been recorded in the
past.

71. Llanwrda Shingle Beds (SN720310) —
The best example of undisturbed river shingle on
the Afon Tywi consisting of a mixture of deposits
ranging from sand and fine gravels through to
coarse pebbles. The expanses of exposed shingle
are bordered by shallow backwaters and willow
carr. A characteristic fauna includes national
rarities such as the beetles *Coccinella 5-punctata*,
Lionychus quadrillum and *Fleutiauxellus maritimus*
and the predatory shingle flies *Tachydromia
acklandi* and *T. halidayi*.

72. Montgomery Canal (SO139930 —
SJ245213) — Approximately twenty-two
kilometres of the Shropshire Union Canal are
contained within Powys, from Newtown to
Llanymynech. The canal closed in 1936 but an
eight kilometre stretch has been restored north of
Welshpool. The submerged macrophyte
community is of national importance, its diversity
reflecting differences in management and water
quality which are also evident in the distributions
of aquatic and marginal invertebrate
communities. Overall the fauna is typical of
clean, productive lowland waters but includes a
number of national rarities, particularly amongst
the water beetles and freshwater molluscs. The
canal is owned and managed by the British
Waterways Board.

73. Mynydd Illtyd (SN965257) — An area of
open moorland with watershed mires at 325 m
a.s.l, within the Brecon Beacons National Park.
Some of the pools within the mires are fed by
lime-rich water and the surrounding fen supports
a number of scarce calcareous plants, including
great fen-sedge and slender sedge. Fourteen
species of dragonfly have been recorded and the
spider fauna includes several uncommon species
of marshy habitats. The site is deserving of
further study in a broader range of invertebrate
groups. Part of the site is managed as a nature
reserve by the Brecknock Wildlife Trust.

74. **Nant Sere** (SO035239) — Open, montane birchwood on the northern slope of the Brecon Beacons with a high proportion of rowan and hawthorn in the sparse shrub layer. The woodland is extensively flushed and there are many fallen birches which are in varying stages of decomposition. Mature alders dominate the wetter ground. The humid conditions and abundance of dead wood favour many species of upland invertebrates and the site is regarded as being of national importance for fungus gnats and craneflies, including the nationally rare *Gonomyia limbata*. Other valley birchwoods in this area, particularly Cwm Llwch and Cwm Oergwm are also worthy of detailed survey. Owned by the National Trust and leased to the Brecknock Wildlife Trust.

75. **Ogof Ffynnon Ddu NNR** (SN867155) — One of the largest, and biologically the best-known, cave systems in Britain, its complex passages extend for approximately 45 kms within Carboniferous rocks at the northern edge of the South Wales Coalfield. The cave fauna includes a number of troglobites, notably the amphipod *Crangonyx subterraneus* and the ostracod *Cypridopsis subterranea*, both of which are known from very few sites in Britain.

76. **Rheidol Floodplain Gravels** (SN606803 — SN646802) — The lower reaches of the Afon Rheidol contain three areas of riparian shingle, situated at Glandwr, Glanyrafon and Dolcniw, which support nationally important invertebrate communities. Nationally rare beetles include *Lionychus quadrillum*, *Coccinella 5-punctata* and *Perileptus areolatus* and the invertebrate interest is enhanced by the backwaters and floodplain carr which flank the point-bar gravels at each site.

77. **Rhosgoch NNR** (SO195485) — A variety of mire communities occupy the shallow valley floor of this sixty hectare reserve. The central raised acidic mire is surrounded by well-developed carr which grades into extensive areas of poor-fen, particularly in the south-western half of the valley. A limited amount of casual invertebrate recording has indicated the site's potential for wetland invertebrates. Of particular interest is the large population of the ground beetle *Blethisa multipunctata*, a species of seasonally-flooded fens which has declined nationally as a result of wetland drainage.

78. **Rhos Llawr-cwrt NNR** (SN410499) — The site consists of several large enclosures of unimproved sedge-rich grassland with pingo basin fens and extensive flushes. A major feature is the presence of one of the largest colonies of marsh fritillaries *Eurodryas aurinia* in Britain and there is a wide range of notable phytophagous insects associated with the herb-rich pasture. A colony of the small red damselfly *Ceriagrion tenellum* is present on the pingo fens.

79. **River Severn** (SN822898 — SJ343157) — The Powys section of the River Severn runs from its source on the slopes of Pumlumon to the English border. The upper reaches are stony and fast-flowing but the river takes on a more lowland character as it approaches Newtown and winds through a broad floodplain. Freshwater invertebrates are well-represented, with notable assemblages of Trichoptera, Ephemeroptera and Plecoptera, and the club-tailed dragonfly *Gomphus vulgatissimus* has strong populations in the slow-flowing stretches.

80. **River Usk** (SN818239 — SO245162) — The River Usk rises on the northern slopes of the Black Mountains and, after emerging from the Usk Reservoir, heads east to the Gwent border at Gilwern. The lower stretches of the river pass through fertile floodplain with sandy banks which are important for riparian invertebrates. The freshwater pearl mussel *Margaritifera margaritifera* is known from the stony upper reaches.

81. **River Wye** (SN801870 — SO243470) — Rises on the eastern slopes of Pumlumon where the river is fast-flowing over a stony bed until it reaches Builth Wells. From here to the English border east of Hay-on-Wye, the river meanders through a broad floodplain on Old Red Sandstone. Riffle sections in these middle reaches have provided most records of rare aquatic invertebrates, including the riffle beetle *Stenelmis canaliculata*. Slower-flowing stretches support several dragonfly species such as the white-legged damselfly *Platycnemis pennipes*. The clean waters of the Wye above Builth Wells are also important for freshwater crayfish *Austropotamobius pallipes*.

82. **St David's Head** (SM731272) — Hard rock coastal cliffs, overlain in places by wind-blown sand (Whitesand Bay) and boulder-clay. Coastal heath and cliff grassland communities are well-developed and the favourable climate promotes a rich insect fauna. Bare exposures of sand and soil contribute to the wealth of bees and wasps and contain a population of the regionally scarce purse-web spider *Atypus affinis*. Part owned by the National Trust.

83. **Skokholm Island** (SM736050) — Shares many similarities with nearby Skomer Island and was historically well-recorded although there is a need for more up-to-date information. Nationally scarce invertebrates from many different orders have been recorded, including several moths such as *Bembecia muscaeformis*, *Polymixis xanthomista* and *Eilema griseola*. Springs and seasonally-inundated depressions support an interesting fauna of aquatic Hemiptera and Coleoptera. Managed by the Dyfed Wildlife Trust.

84. **Skomer NNR** (SM725095) — This island nature reserve off the coast of Pembrokeshire contains a variety of maritime grassland and sea-cliff habitats modified by the activities of seabirds and rabbits. The invertebrate fauna is of special interest for its contribution to the study of biogeographical isolation but also contains a number of scarce coastal species, particularly amongst the Lepidoptera and Coleoptera. Spiders have been well-recorded in the past, including the rare *Oxyptila scabricula*, but there is scope for further survey on a range of invertebrate orders. Skomer Island is managed by the Dyfed Wildlife Trust.

85. **Stackpole NNR** (SR985945) — A composite site consisting of dunes, limestone grassland and secondary woodland along with the coastal marl lakes of Bosherston (considered separately). The dune fauna has been reasonably well-studied and includes a large population of the snail *Theba pisana*. The whole area is of considerable importance for aculeate Hymenoptera with a number of national rarities such as *Coelioxys mandibularis*. Owned by the National Trust.

86. **Talley Lakes** (SN632335) — These two lakes cover an area of approximately 18 hectares and occupy kettle-holes in glacial deposits. They are naturally mineral-rich and exhibit a well-marked vegetational sequence from open water and marginal fen, through reedswamp to alder carr. Currently underworked, although rarities such as the reed beetle *Donacia obscura* and the meniscus midge *Dixella amphibia* indicate the site's potential.

87. **Tanybwlch** (SN580803) — The shingle beach which deflects the Afon Ystwyth northwards to Aberystwyth harbour contains the best example of shingle vegetation in the Region and supports a representative invertebrate fauna. Along the river itself, shingle banks within the tidal reach have an unusual beetle community which includes a mixture of riparian and maritime species, including *Aepus marinus*, *Bembidion maritimum* and *Deleaster dichrous*. The rare money spider *Caviphantes saxetorum*, which lives beneath boulders embedded in river gravels, is also present along with the shingle wolf spider *Arctosa cinerea*.

88. **Tynbedw-Grogwynion** (SN700718) — Three kilometres of gravel-bed floodplain on the Afon Ystwyth with extensive banks of bare gravel and several hectares of shingle heath. The gravels have a fauna typical of the Afon Ystwyth with the beetles *Brachygluta pandellei* and *Bibloplectus minutissimus* amongst the scarcer inhabitants and the northern spider *Arctosa cinerea* is abundant. The shingle heath fauna is relatively unknown but includes the notable carabids *Pterostichus lepidus* and *Amara equestris*. Managed as a nature reserve by the Dyfed Wildlife Trust.

89. **Ty'n-yr-helyg** (SN595765) — A small shingle bank on the north side of the Afon Ystwyth, backing onto an area of acidic grassland and mature gorse and broom scrub. The site has an exceptional shingle beetle fauna with *Lionychus quadrillum*, *Coccinella 5-punctata*, *Thinobius newberyi* and *Lathrobium dilutum*. The tiny water beetle *Bidessus minutissimus* is common in shallow water at the edge of the gravels.

90. **West Williamston** (SN026060) — Tidal creeks and botanically-rich saltmarsh penetrate into the disused Carboniferous Limestone quarries on the south bank of the Cresswell River. The limestone grassland and woodland habitats are, as yet, poorly-worked for invertebrates but the ungrazed saltmarsh has an excellent beetle fauna which includes *Polydrusus pulchellus*, *Brachygluta simplex* and *Amara convexiuscula*. West Williamston is owned by the National Trust and managed by the Dyfed Wildlife Trust.

91. **Ynys Eidiol** (SN671952) — A relict area of raised mire on the Dyfi floodplain with a mixture of wetland habitats including reedswamp and bog myrtle scrub. This outlier of the Cors Fochno system supports a colony of the rosy marsh moth *Eugraphe subrosea* and the rare money spider *Maso gallicus*.

92. **Ynyslas, Dyfi NNR** (SN605939) — This is a well-developed dune system at the mouth of the Dyfi estuary with a good succession from fixed dunes through to dune slacks and reedswamps. Huge populations of the woodlouse *Armadillidium album* are present in strandline debris and the dung beetle *Aphodius plagiatus* is also frequent

here. Typical moths and butterflies of the western dunes are well-represented.

93. **Ynys Uchaf** (SN490150) — An extensive floodplain mire with rich fen communities and well-developed willow and alder carr. The fauna has not been comprehensively sampled but casual recording has recently produced nationally scarce species such as *Blethisa multipunctata, Abagous lutulentus* and *Vanoyia tenuicornis*.

South Wales

94. Aberthaw Leys (ST042658) — A small but important site with botanically-diverse saltmarsh communities supporting a good range of characteristic and scarce invertebrates, particularly amongst the phytophagous Coleoptera. Sandy creeks back onto a shingle ridge which abuts limestone cliffs at the eastern end. The bombadier beetle *Brachinus crepitans* occurs on the cliff grassland and aculeate Hymenoptera are abundant but as yet little studied. The Leys is a nature reserve managed by the Glamorgan Wildlife Trust.

95. Brockwell's Meadow (ST469897) — Unimproved calcareous pastures and hay meadows on Carboniferous Limestone and Triassic Sandstone. The chief importance of this site lies in the population of the hornet robber fly *Asilus crabroniformis* but great green bush crickets *Tettigonia viridissima* are also present. Further surveys should reveal that the fauna associated with the rich flora of these ancient grasslands is also of interest.

96. Cleddon Bog (SO509039) — The best remaining lowland mire in Gwent, Cleddon Bog is largely dominated by heather and purple moor-grass. It is almost surrounded by woodland and the sheltered environment and scrub edge are beneficial features for invertebrates. A typical fauna of such acidic fens occurs here, including the scarce peatland spiders *Glyphesis servulus* and *Lepthyphantes insignis*.

97. Crymlyn Bog (SS695945) — Situated on the eastern outskirts of Swansea, Crymlyn Bog is the largest area of lowland fen in Wales. A wide range of wetland communities have developed in the wake of a complex geomorphological history, resulting effectively in a broad shallow basin of some 240 hectares. There are similarities amongst both the plant and invertebrate communities with the East Anglian fens, making Crymlyn Bog and the adjoining Pant-y-Sais (q.v.) unique in a Welsh context. Part of Crymlyn Bog is a National Nature Reserve.

98. Ffrwd Farm (SN420026) — An area of species-rich fen with reedswamp and carr on the Pembrey Levels. The presence of the scarce fenland soldier beetle *Silis ruficollis* demonstrates affinities with Crymlyn Bog. The hairy dragonfly *Brachytron pratense* is frequent on the internal ditches and a representative selection of fenland

moths has been recorded. Ffrwd Farm is a nature reserve which is jointly managed by the Dyfed Wildlife Trust and the Llanelli Naturalist's Society.

99. Gwent Levels (ST222378 to ST4987) — The Gwent Levels constitute the most extensive area of grazing marsh in Wales. Within this vast area of reclaimed wet pasture there is an estimated 1400 kilometres of ditches, chiefly on estuarine clays but there are also a number of ditches in fen peat. The quality and extent of the habitat is reflected in the range of nationally scarce invertebrates present and the Gwent Levels are of undoubted national importance for several groups of aquatic and semi-aquatic invertebrates.

100. Kenfig Burrows (SS792808) — A large dune system with valuable habitat examples throughout the dune succession from strandline, through dune slacks, to mature dune grassland. Kenfig Pool at the back of the dunes is a 32 hectare shallow lake with fringing reedbeds and a good dragonfly fauna. The dune invertebrates are typical of such systems on the South Wales coast but one particular speciality is the weevil *Tychius quinquepunctatus* which is known from very few British sites. Kenfig is a National Nature Reserve administered by Mid Glamorgan County Council.

101. Llangennith Burrows (SS410915) — A narrow strip of west-facing dunes at the tip of the Gower peninsula. Llangennith (and the contiguous Broughton Burrows) has a characteristically rich dune fauna, although some parts of the site are suffering erosion from tourist pressures. At Spaniard Rocks there are important freshwater seepages across the beach which support the nationally rare fly *Dolichopus signifer*.

102. Machynys (SS513979) — Three small flooded brick-pits on the outskirts of Llanelli support a remarkable range of coastal fen invertebrates, including populations of the hairy dragonfly *Brachytron pratense* and the variable damselfly *Coenagrion pulchellum*. The richest elements of the fauna are associated with the marginal and inter-linking belts of tall fen where an important selection of scarce wetland beetles, moths and flies has been recorded. The nearby shingle beach and saltmarsh at Penrhyngwyn on the Burry Inlet are also of considerable invertebrate interest.

103. **Magor Marsh** (ST425866) — This Gwent Wildlife Trust reserve at the eastern end of the Gwent Levels is the largest remant of formerly extensive fenlands. Much of the site is covered by rich sedge fen and fen meadow and there are also areas of reedswamp and willow carr. The terrestrial fauna is outstanding in a Welsh context with, for example, the ground beetles *Trechus discus*, *Pterostichus anthracinus* and *Oodes helopioides* and a good range of phytophagous beetles typical of rich fenland. There is also demonstrated interest in the aquatic fauna of the internal ditch system.

104. **Margam Moors** (SS78-84-) — An area of grazing levels sandwiched between Margam Burrows and Eglwys Nunydd Reservoir. Brief surveys have shown that a representative fauna is present in the ditch system, including rarities such as the water beetle *Haliplus mucronatus*. Away from the Gwent Levels, this is one of very few grazing levels of conservation significance in Wales and further invertebrate surveys are desirable.

105. **Merthyr Mawr Warren** (SS861768) — Arguably the richest of the South Wales dune systems in entomological terms, Merthyr Mawr is unique in that the dunes overlie and abut steep Carboniferous Limestone ridges. This gives added variety to the dune topography, providing shelter and sunny banks throughout this vast area. Bees and wasps are particularly well represented with several national rarities and many other invertebrate groups also have important faunas. A full dune succession through to ash woodland supports an extensive range of scarce invertebrates, including wetland flies in the dune slacks and the ground beetle *Nebria complanata* on the strandline.

106. **Nant Glais Caves** (SO040105) — The cave system of Ogof-y-ci in Carboniferous Limestone on the edge of the Brecon Beacons National Park is one of only two British localities known for the troglobitic spider *Porrhomma rosenhaueri*. Other subterranean invertebrates present include the cave shrimp *Niphargus fontanus* and the aquatic woodlouse *Proasellus cavaticus*.

107. **Oxwich Bay** (SS506870) — An outstanding complex of high quality habitats on the south coast of the Gower peninsula. The mixture of coastal cliffs, ancient woodland, sand dunes, saltmarsh and freshwater marsh is unparalleled in the Region and inevitably supports an immense and important invertebrate fauna. Each of the main habitat components is of interest in its own right, from the aculeate-rich head deposits of the western cliffs to the remarkable assemblages of Diptera in the old woodlands. Oxwich Bay is undoubtedly of national importance for the conservation of invertebrates and has a long tradition of entomological recording but such a large area still holds scope for further surveys. Approximately two-thirds of the Oxwich Bay SSSI is managed as a National Nature Reserve.

108. **Pant-y-Sais** (SS716942) — Effectively an eastern extension of Crymlyn Bog (q.v.), although now hydrologically separate. There are obvious similarities between the faunas of the two sites. Pant-y-Sais is a Local Nature Reserve administered by Neath Borough Council. The reserve contains a range of acidic & rich fen communities and is one of the few Welsh localities for the fenland ground beetle *Odacantha melanura*.

109. **Pembrey Forest** (SN39-02-) — Sand dunes formerly occupied much of the land between Kidweli and Burry Port but much of this was afforested with Corsican pines about sixty years ago. The broad forest rides and glades are still of invertebrate interest, however, as they support a mature dune grassland flora which harbours a good variety of typical invertebrates and the sheltered conditions make this one of the best butterfly sites in Carmarthenshire. A pond in the middle of the forest, which was created from a former dune slack, has an exceptional fauna of snail-killing flies. At least nineteen species have been recorded, including *Pteromicra leucopeza*, *P. glabricula*, *Colobaea bifasciella*, *Sciomyza simplex* and *Pherbellia nana*. Pembrey Forest is owned by the Forestry Commission and is designated as a Forest Nature Reserve.

110. **River Monnow** (SO328258 — SO509139) — The Monnow rises on the slopes of the Black Mountains in Herefordshire and at 3 km above its junction with the Afon Honddu forms the border between England and Wales until it reaches the River Wye at Monmouth. It is predominantly stony with deep pools and long riffles and for much of its length there are bankside stretches of silt or sand. Both the aquatic and riparian invertebrate faunas are of exceptional quality, reflecting the unmodified and unpolluted nature of the river channel and its banks.

111. **River Usk** (SO230162 — ST317836) — Entering South Wales Region to the west of

Abergavenny, the Usk heads southwards to Newport and the sea. Although not as well known entomologically as the Monnow, there are obvious similarities between the two rivers, with a rich dipteran fauna known from the banks of the Usk in its lower reaches. Further information on other aspects of the invertebrate fauna is desirable.

112. **River Wye** (SO527154 — ST534942) — This lower stretch of the River Wye, most of which acts as the border between England and Wales, flows through a gorge in the Carboniferous Limestone of the Forest of Dean and is tidal below Bigsweir Bridge. The aquatic fauna is generally typical of stony streams but quieter stretches with beds of water-crowfoot support populations of the club-tailed dragonfly *Gomphus vulgatissimus* and the white-legged damselfly *Platycnemis pennipes*. The rare mayfly *Potamanthus luteus*, which is only known with certainty from the Rivers Thames, Usk and Wye, has been recorded from the Welsh section of the river.

113. **Tywyn Burrows** (SN36-05-) — A rich and varied dune complex at the mouth of the Gwendraeth River, south-west of Kidweli. Tywyn Burrows has good examples of embryo dune, dune grassland, dune slack and saltmarsh habitats, each of which has a representative fauna and a number of nationally scarce species. Of prime importance is the population of the ground beetle *Panageus crux-major*, here at its only known British locality, and the slacks also support Cepero's groundhopper *Tetrix ceperoi* at the northern limit of its range. Owned by the Ministry of Defence.

114. **Whiteford Burrows** (SS450955) — Whiteford Burrows is situated on the north side of the Gower peninsula at the mouth of the Burry Inlet. The dune spit extends northwards for three kilometres, sheltering the saltmarsh expanse of Landimore Marsh on its eastern side. Forming a border between the dunes and the saltmarsh is a linear seepage marsh, one of the best examples of this type of transition zone in Britain and an important habitat for a number of scarce wetland flies. Whiteford Burrows is a National Nature Reserve.

115. **Wye Valley Woods** (ST53-97-) — The ancient woodlands of the Lower Wye Valley between Chepstow and Monmouth are an outstanding example of mixed deciduous gorge woodlands of great importance for nature conservation. Many areas of the steep cliff woodlands are difficult to survey and little is known of their invertebrate fauna but one of the best sections is the complex of woods at Wyndcliffe, which is managed under a Forest Nature Reserve Agreement with the Forestry Commission. The high forest on the Carboniferous Limestone here is dominated in places by ash and wych elm. There are also large stands of small-leaved lime, a foodplant for the nationally rare scarce hook-tip moth *Sabra harpagula*. The Lepidoptera are comparatively well-recorded but other elements of the invertebrate fauna would repay detailed survey.

Appendix 2

Organisations associated with the conservation of invertebrates in Wales

Brecknock Wildlife Trust
Lion House, 7 Lion Street, Brecon, Powys, LD3 7AY.

Brecon Beacons National Park
6 Glamorgan Street, Brecon, Powys, LD3 7DP.

British Butterfly Conservation Society
South Wales Branch, c/o N. Jones, 31 Drummau Road, Birchgrove, Swansea, SA7 9QA
Gwynedd Branch, c/o Mrs L. Harrison, 19 Gwel Eryri, Llandegfan, Ynys Mon, Gwynedd.
Merseyside and Clwyd Branch, c/o R. Whitehead, 'Haulfryn', Graigfechan, Clwyd, LL15 2HA.

Cardiff Naturalists' Society Entomological Section
c/o D.A. Edwards, 98 Clodien Avenue, Cardiff, South Glamorgan, CF4 3NQ

Clwyd Entomological Society
c/o B. Formstone, 15 Beech Avenue, Gresford, Clwyd, LL12 8EL.

Countryside Council for Wales
Bala sub-office, Midland Bank Chambers, 56 High Street, Bala, Gwynedd, LL23 7AB.
Clwyd sub-office, Victoria House, Grosvenor Street, Mold, Clwyd, CH7 1EJ.
Dolgellau sub-office, Victoria Building, Meyrick Street, Dolgellau, Gwynedd, Ll40 1ZR.
Dyfed and Mid Wales Regional Office, Plas Gogerddan, Aberystwyth, Dyfed, SY23 3EE.
Fishguard sub-office, The Flat, Sycamore Lodge, Hamilton Street, Fishguard, Dyfed, SA65 9HL.
Llandeilo sub-office, 56 Rhosmaen Street, Llandeilo, Dyfed, SA19 6HA.
Llandrindod Wells sub-office, Third floor, Gwalia, Ithon Road, Llandrindod Wells, Powys, LD1 6AA.
Mold sub-office, Victoria House, Grosvenor Street, Mold, Clwyd, CH7 1EJ.
Newtown sub-office, Ladywell House, Park Street, Newtown, Powys, SY15 1RO.
North Wales Regional Office, Hafod Elfyn, Ffordd Penrhos, Bangor, Gwynedd, LL57 2LQ.
Oxwich sub-office, Oxwich Reserve Centre, Oxwich, Swansea, West Glamorgan, SA3 1LS.
South Wales Regional Office, 43 The Parade, Roath, Cardiff, CF2 3UH.

Dyfed Invertebrate Group
c/o Countryside Council for Wales, Plas Gogerddan, Aberystwyth, Dyfed, SY23 3EE.

Dyfed Wildlife Trust
7 Market Street, Haverfordwest, Dyfed, SA61 1NF.

Glamorgan Dragonfly Survey Group
c/o S. Moon, Kenfig Nature Reserve, Ton Kenfig, Pyle, Mid Glamorgan, CF33 4PT

Glamorgan Wildlife Trust
Glamorgan Nature Centre, Fountain Road, Tondu, Bridgend, Mid Glamorgan, CF32 OEH

Great Orme's Head Country Park
Warden, Aberconwy Borough Council, Town Hall, Llandudno, Gwynedd.

Gwent Wildlife Trust
16 White Swan Court, Monmouth, Gwent, NP5 3NY

Yr Wyddfa, Gwynedd: This rock-strewn grassland is the haunt of the mountain's most famous invertebrate, the "Snowdon beetle" *Chrysolina cerealis*. Scattered tufts of wild thyme amongst the close-grazed sward are the foodplant of both the larvae and the adults of this national rarity. (Photograph by A.P. Fowles.)

***Chrysolina cerealis* (Coleoptera):** The rainbow leaf beetle is confined in Britain to the thyme-rich grassland on high mountain slopes in Snowdonia. It is a protected species on Schedule 5 of the Wildlife and Countryside Act, 1981. (Photograph by M. Hammett.)

***Xestia ashworthii* (Lepidoptera):** Although the caterpillars of this moth feed on a wide range of foodplants, Ashworth's rustic is restricted in Britain to the mountains of northern Wales. (Photograph by A.P. Fowles.)

Cadair Idris, Gwynedd: Exposed mountain summits support a range of species adapted to survive in this bleak environment. Upland peaks with scree or scattered rocks are often the richest sites for invertebrates as shelter is vitally important on high ground. (Photograph by A.P. Fowles.)

Craig Cerrig Gleisiad, Powys: The Brecon Beacons are less well-known entomologically than most of the other major upland blocks in Wales and there is considerable potential for exciting discoveries amongst their spectacular landscapes.
(Photograph by NCC.)

Nebria gyllenhali **(Coleoptera):** This upland ground beetle is local but widespread in the mountainous districts of Wales. It is usually found under stones, often at the edge of streams or flushes.
(Photograph by R.S. Key.)

Migneint, Gwynedd: Vast areas of blanket mire clothe level ground on the upland plateaux in many parts of Wales.
(Photograph by A.P. Fowles.)

Figyn Blaen-brefi, Dyfed: This watershed mire is a haunt of the caddisfly *Oxyethira mirabilis*, a speciality of upland peat bogs.
(Photograph by A.O. Chater.)

Institute of Terrestrial Ecology
Bangor Research Unit, University College of North Wales, Deiniol Road, Bangor, Gwynedd, LL57 2UP.

Llanelli Naturalists Society
c/o R.D. Pryce, Trevethin, Pwll, Llanelli, Dyfed, SA15 4AL.

Montgomery Wildlife Trust
8 Severn Square, Newtown, Powys, SY16 2AG.

National Rivers Authority
Welsh Region (North), Area Conservation, Fisheries and Recreation Officer, Highfield, Priestly Road, Caernarfon, Gwynedd.
Welsh Region (South-east), Area Conservation, Fisheries and Recreation Officer, Plas-yr-afon, St Mellons Business Park, Cardiff, CF3 0LT.
Welsh Region (South-west), Area Conservation, Fisheries and Recreation Officer, Hawthorn Rise, Haverfordwest, Dyfed, SA61 2BH.
Severn Trent Region (Upper Severn), Area Conservation, Fisheries and Recreation Officer, Hafren House, Welshpool Road, Shelton, Shrewsbury, SY3 8BB.

The National Trust
North Wales — Trinity Square, Llandudno, Gwynedd, LL30 2DE.
South Wales — The King's Head, Bridge Street, Llandeilo, Dyfed, SA19 6BB.

North Wales Invertebrate Group
c/o Mrs M.J. Morgan, School of Animal Biology, University College of North Wales, Bangor, Gwynedd, LL57 2UW.

North Wales Wildlife Trust
376 High Street, Bangor, Gwynedd, LL57 1YE.

Pembrokeshire Coast National Park
County Offices, St Thomas's Green, Haverfordwest, Dyfed, SA61 1QZ.

Radnorshire Wildlife Trust
1 Gwalia Annexe, Ithon Road, Llandrindod Wells, Powys, LD1 6AS.

Royal Society for the Protection of Birds (Wales Office)
Bryn Aderyn, The Bank, Newtown, Powys, SY16 2AB.

Snowdonia National Park
National Park Office, Penrhyndeudraeth, Gwynedd, LL48 6LS.

Woodland Trust
Autumn Park, Dysart Road, Grantham, Lincolnshire, NG31 6LL.

Appendix 3

Selected bibliography

Key to symbols:

N Publications relevant to North Wales Region
M Publications relevant to Dyfed-Powys Region
S Publications relevant to South Wales Region

Alexander, K.N.A. 1987. Soldier beetles in Dyfed. *Dyfed Invertebrate Group Newsletter,* No. 5: 11-12. **M, S**

Askew, R.R. 1974. Insects from Bardsey Island. *Entomologist's Gazette, 25*: 45-51. **N**

Badcock, R.M. 1949. Studies in stream life in tributaries of the Welsh Dee. *Journal of Animal Ecology, 18*: 193-208. **N**

Balfour-Browne, J. 1942. The aquatic Coleoptera (including Hydrophilidae, Sphaeridiinae) of North Wales. *Entomologist's Monthly Magazine, 78*: 273-280. **N**

Balfour-Browne, F. 1949. The water beetles found in the counties of Cheshire, Flintshire, Denbighshire, Caernarvonshire, Anglesey, Merionethshire and Montgomeryshire. *Cheshire and North Wales Natural History, 3*: 81-134. **N, M**

Barber, A.D. 1988. Dyfed centipedes. *Dyfed Invertebrate Group Newsletter,* No. 10: 1-9. **M, S**

Barker, T.W. 1905. *Handbook to the natural history of Carmarthenshire.* Carmarthen, Spurrell & Sons. (A list of Carmarthenshire butterflies and moths, pp 21-34.) **M, S**

Barnes, H.F. 1924. Preliminary list of the crane-flies of Carnarvonshire, N. Wales. *Entomologist's Monthly Magazine, 60*: 225-227. **N**

Barnes, H.F. 1925. The ecological distribution of adult crane-flies in Carnarvonshire. *Journal of Ecology, 13*: 138-148. **N**

Barnes, H.F. 1926. The crane-flies of Carnarvonshire. *North Western Naturalist, 1*: 17-34. **N**

Blacker, N.C. 1989. The ants (Hym.: Formicidae) of the Gower peninsula, West Glamorgan, South Wales. *Entomologist's Record and Journal of Variation, 101*: 261-266. **S**

Blower, J.G. 1989. The Myriapoda of Gower. *Bulletin of the British Myriapod Group,* No. 6: 14-22. **S**

Boyce, D.C. 1988. Deadwood beetles in Ceredigion (VC46). *Dyfed Invertebrate Group Newsletter,* No. 11: 13-15. **M**

Boyce, D.C. 1990. The beetles of Ynyslas Dunes (22/6094), Dyfi NNR, Ceredigion (VC46). *Dyfed Invertebrate Group Newsletter,* No. 18: 5-14. **M**

Briggs, J.D., *ed.* 1988. *Montgomery Canal Ecological Survey. Survey report 1985-1988.* Llanymynech, Montgomery Canal Ecological Survey. **M**

Brittain, J.E. 1974. Ephemeroptera and Plecoptera in North Wales. *Entomologist's Monthly Magazine, 110*: 247-251. **N**

Brooker, M.P., & Morris, D.L. 1980. A survey of the macro-invertebrate riffle fauna of the River Wye. *Freshwater Biology, 10*: 437-458. **M**

Brooker, M.P., & Morris, D.L. 1980. A survey of the macro-invertebrate riffle fauna of the Rivers Ystwyth and Rheidol, Wales. *Freshwater Biology, 10*: 459-474. **M**

Brown, E.S. 1943. A contribution towards an ecological survey of the aquatic and semi-aquatic Hemiptera-Heteroptera (water bugs) of the British Isles. Anglesey, Caernarvon and Merioneth. *Transactions of the Society for British Entomology, 8*: 169-230. **N**

Brown, E.S. 1948. The aquatic Coleoptera of North Wales. *Transactions of the Society for British Entomology, 9*: 135-149. **N**

Chatelain, R.G. 1978. *Eriopygodes imbecilla* Hb: the Silurian (Lep.: Noctuidae) in Monmouthshire. *Entomologist's Record and Journal of Variation, 90*: 189. **S**

Chater, A.O. 1986. Woodlice in Ceredigion. *Dyfed Invertebrate Group Newsletter,* No. 2: 3-10. **M**

Chater, A.O. 1986. Recent land mollusc recording in Ceredigion. *Dyfed Invertebrate Group Newsletter,* No. 4: 15-16. **M**

Chater, A.O. 1989. False-scorpions in Ceredigion. *Dyfed Invertebrate Group Newsletter,* No. 14: 5-10. **M**

Chater, A.O. 1991. Bristletails in Ceredigion. *Dyfed Invertebrate Group Newsletter,* No. 22: 1-4. **M**

Chater, A.O., & Spencer, R.A. 1989. The wood ant *Formica rufa* in Ceredigion, VC46. *Dyfed Invertebrate Group Newsletter,* No. 15: 12-17. **M**

Chatfield, J.E. 1974. The Mollusca of the Glamorgan Canal Nature Reserve, Whitchurch. *Glamorgan Naturalists' Trust Annual Bulletin,* No. 13: 13-16. **S**

Clare, P., & Edwards, R.W. 1983. The macro-invertebrate fauna of the drainage channels of the Gwent Levels, South Wales. *Freshwater Biology, 13*: 205-225. **S**

Claridge, M.F., & Reynolds, W.J. 1972. Host plant specificity, oviposition behaviour and egg parasitism in some woodland leafhoppers of the genus *Oncopsis*

(Hemiptera Homoptera: Cicadellidae). *Transactions of the Royal Entomological Society of London, 124*: 149-166. **M, S**

Coker, S., & Fox, A.D. 1985. *West Wales dragonflies.* Clarebeston Road, Mountain Books. **M, S**

Colley, L.T. 1983. *Coenagrion mercuriale* (Charpentier) in Anglesey, North Wales. *Journal of the British Dragonfly Society, 1*: 27. **N**

Cooke, J.A.L., & Cotton, M.J. 1961. Some observations on the ecology of spiders occurring on sand dunes at Whiteford Burrows, Gower peninsula, Glamorgan. *Entomologist's Monthly Magazine, 97*: 183-187. **S**

Cotton, M.J. 1967. Aspects of the ecology of sand dune arthropods. *Entomologist, 100*: 157-165. **S**

Dean, J.D. 1936. Non-marine Mollusca. *In: Glamorgan County History. Vol.1. Natural history,* ed. by W. M. Tattersall, 391-400. Cardiff, W. Lewis. **S**

Dennis, R.H.L. 1970. *Eumenis semele thyone* Thompson (Lep., Satyridae): comparisons and remarks. *Entomologist's Record and Journal of Variation, 82*: 168-175. **N**

Dennis, R.H.L. 1972. A biometrical study of a Welsh colony of the large heath butterfly, *Coenonympha tullia* Muller (Rhopalocera). *Entomologist, 105*: 313-326. **N**

Dennis, R.H.L. 1972. *Eumenis semele* (L.) *thyone* Thompson (Lep., Satyridae). A microgeographical race. *Entomologist's Record and Journal of Variation, 84*: 38-44. **N**

Dillwyn, L.W. 1829. *Memoranda relating to coleopterous insects found in the neighbourhood of Swansea.* Swansea, privately circulated. **S**

Disney, R.H.L. 1972. Some scuttle flies (Dipt., Phoridae) from North Wales. *Nature in Wales, 16*: 25-31. **N**

Drake, C.M. 1986. *A survey of the invertebrates of the Gwent Levels, 1985.* Peterborough, Nature Conservancy Council. (Contract Surveys, No. 1.) **S**

Drake, C.M. 1987. Dragonflies on the Gwent and Somerset Levels and Moors. *Journal of the British Dragonfly Society, 3*: 1-4. **S**

Drake, C.M. 1988. Diptera from the Gwent Levels, South Wales. *Entomologist's Monthly Magazine, 124*: 37-44. **S**

Drake, C.M. 1988. Water beetles from the Gwent Levels, Wales. *Balfour-Browne Club Newsletter,* No. 43: 13-15. **S**

Duffey, E. 1968. An ecological analysis of the spider fauna of sand dunes. *Journal of Animal Ecology, 37*: 641-674. **S**

Duffey, E. 1970. Habitat selection by spiders on a saltmarsh in Gower. *Nature in Wales, 12*: 15-23. **S**

Dunn, D.R. 1961. The bottom fauna of Llyn Tegid (Lake Bala), Merionethshire. *Journal of Animal Ecology, 30*: 267-281. **N**

Elliott, P., & King, P.E. 1986. A comparison of the environmental adaptations of the larval and imaginal stages of certain intertidal Coleoptera. *Entomologist's Monthly Magazine, 122*: 177-184. **S**

Evans, F. 1989. *A review of the management of lowland wet heath in Dyfed, West Wales.* Peterborough, Nature Conservancy Council. (Contract Surveys No. 42.) **M**

Foster, G.N. 1971. The distribution of aquatic Coleoptera in Anglesey. *Entomologist's Gazette, 22*: 47-54. **N**

Foster, G.N. 1988. Aquatic Coleoptera in Dyfed. *Dyfed Invertebrate Group Newsletter,* No. 11: 1-6. **M, S**

Foster, G.N., & Lazell, M. 1967. Aquatic Coleoptera on Anglesey. *Entomologist's Monthly Magazine, 103*: 197-202. **N**

Fowles, A.P. 1986. The butterflies of Ceredigion. *Nature in Wales (New Series), 3* (1984): 25-43. **M**

Fowles, A.P. 1986. Crickets and grasshoppers in Dyfed. *Dyfed Invertebrate Group Newsletter,* No. 1: 7-12. **M, S**

Fowles, A.P. 1987. An investigation of the effects of fire upon the invertebrate fauna of a coastal raised mire. *Dyfed Invertebrate Group Newsletter,* No. 8: 4-8. **M**

Fowles, A.P. 1988. *The moths of Ceredigion.* Peterborough, Nature Conservancy Council. (Research and Survey in Nature Conservation, No. 8.) **M**

Fowles, A.P. 1989. The Coleoptera of shingle banks on the River Ystwyth, Dyfed. *Entomologists's Record and Journal of Variation, 101*: 209-222. **M**

Fowles, A.P. 1991. An introduction to the snail-killing flies (Diptera: Sciomyzidae) of Ceredigion. *Dyfed Invertebrate Group Newsletter,* No. 22: 14-22. **M**

Fowles, A.P., & Boyce, D.C. 1991. The coleopterous fauna of soft-rock cliff habitats at Porth Neigwl, Llŷn. *North Wales Invertebrate Group Newsletter,* No. 4: 6. **N**

Fowles, A.P., Dobson, S., & Morgan, I.K. 1991. A provisional account of the spider fauna of Dyfed. *Dyfed Invertebrate Group Newsletter,* No. 21: 1-16. **M, S**

Fox, A.D. 1986. Effects of ditch-blockage on adult Odonata at a coastal raised mire site in central west Wales, United Kingdom. *Odonatologica, 15*: 327-334. **M**

George, R.S. 1989. A brief summary of the fleas of the vice-counties of Cardigan, Carmarthen & Pembroke and the islands of Cardigan, Ramsey, Skokholm & Skomer. *Dyfed Invertebrate Group Newsletter,* No. 14: 10-18. **M, S**

Gilbert, O. 1956. The natural histories of four species of *Calathus* (Coleoptera, Carabidae) living on sand dunes in Anglesey, North Wales. *Oikos, 7*: 22-47. **N**

Goodier, R. 1967. Welsh mountain spiders. *Nature in Wales, 10*: 106-114. **N, M**

Goodier, R. 1968. Welsh mountain beetles. *Nature in Wales, 11*: 2-11. **N, M**

Goodier, R. 1970. Notes on mountain spiders from Wales. *Bulletin of the British Arachnological Society, 1*: 85-87, 97-100. **N**

Griffiths, D. 1973. The structure of an acid moorland pond community. *Journal of Animal Ecology, 42*: 263-283. **S**

Gritten, R. 1974. The spiders of Newborough Warren National Nature Reserve. *British Arachnological Society, Secretary's News Letter, No. 11*: 8-9. **N**

Hallett, H.M. 1917. The Lepidoptera of Glamorgan. *Transactions of the Cardiff Naturalists' Society, 50*: 45-86. **S**

Hallett, H.M. 1929. The Neuroptera of Glamorgan. *Transactions of the Cardiff Naturalists' Society, 62*: 67-69. **S**

Hallett, H.M. 1929. The Orthoptera of Glamorgan. *Transactions of the Cardiff Naturalists' Society, 62*: 70-72. **S**

Hallett, H.M. 1932. The sawflies of Glamorgan. *Transactions of the Cardiff Naturalists' Society, 63*: 53-61. **S**

Hallett, H.M. 1936. Insects of Glamorgan. *In: Glamorgan County History. Vol.1. Natural history*, ed. by W. M. Tattersall, 312-375. Cardiff, W. Lewis **S**

Harding, P.T. 1971. Notes on the occurrence of woodlice (Isopoda: Oniscoidea) on sand dunes at Whiteford Burrows, Glamorgan. *Entomologist, 104*: 98-103. **S**

Hildrew, A.G., & Edington, J.M. 1979. Factors facilitating the coexistence of hydropsychid caddis larvae (Trichoptera) in the same river system. *Journal of Animal Ecology, 48*: 557-576. **S**

Hope Jones, P. 1986. The grayling butterfly on Bardsey: some exploratory investigations. *Bardsey Observatory Report, No. 30*: 70-78. **N**

Horton, G.A.N. 1967. Moths of the Usk and Wye Valleys. *Monmouthshire Wildlife Report, No. 4*: 17-25. **S**

Horton, G.A.N. 1988. The history of the marsh fritillary in Gwent. *Gwent Wildlife Trust Newsletter, No. 62*: 4-6. **S**

Hughes, M.O. 1990. Some observations on the Syrphidae (Diptera) of the counties of Clwyd and Gwynedd, Wales. *Amateur Entomologist's Society Bulletin, 49*: 165-171. **N**

Hughes, M.R. 1983. The land and freshwater Mollusca of the Glamorgan Canal Nature Reserve. *Conchologist's Newsletter, No. 86*: 121-125. **S**

Hunt, P.C., & Jones, J.W. 1972. The effect of water level fluctuations on a littoral fauna. *Journal of Fish Biology, 4*: 385-394. **N**

Hynes, H.B.N. 1961. The effect of water level fluctuations on littoral fauna. *Verhandlungen der Internationalen Vereinigung fur Theoretische und Angewandte Limnologie, 14*: 652-656. **N**

Jackson, A.R. 1936. Arachnida of Glamorgan. *In: Glamorgan County History. Vol.1. Natural history*, ed. by W. M. Tattersall, 383-390. Cardiff, W. Lewis. **S**

Jefferson, G.T., & Chapman, P.R.J. 1979. *Studies on the invertebrate fauna of the Ogof Ffynnon Ddu cave system.* (Contractor: University College of Wales, Cardiff). Unpublished report to Nature Conservancy Council. **M**

Jenkins, R.A. 1979. Records of Trichoptera from south-west Wales. *Entomologist's Gazette, 30*: 31-43. **M**

Jenkins, R.A., Wade, K.R., & Pugh, E. 1984. Macroinvertebrate-habitat relationships in the River Teifi catchment and the significance to conservation. *Freshwater Biology, 14*: 23-42. **M**

Johnson, C. 1991. Coleoptera of Merioneth, North Wales: a second supplement to Skidmore & Johnson's list, 1969. *Entomologist's Gazette, 42*: 107-145. **N**

Jones, J.R.E. 1941. The fauna of the River Dovey, West Wales. *Journal of Animal Ecology, 10*: 12-24. **N, M**

Jones, J.R.E. 1943. The fauna of the River Teifi, West Wales. *Journal of Animal Ecology, 12*: 115-123. **M**

Jones, J.R.E. 1948. The fauna of four streams in the 'Black Mountain' district of South Wales. *Journal of Animal Ecology, 17*: 51-65. **M**

Jones, J.R.E. 1949. An ecological study of the River Rheidol, north Cardiganshire, Wales. *Journal of Animal Ecology, 18*: 67-88. **M**

Jones, J.R.E. 1949. A further ecological study of calcareous streams in the 'Black Mountain' district of South Wales. *Journal of Animal Ecology, 18*: 142-159. **M**

Jones, J.R.E. 1951. An ecological study of the River Towy. *Journal of Animal Ecology, 20*: 68-86. **M**

King, P.E., & Stabins, V. 1971. Aspects of the biology of a strand-living beetle *Eurynebria complanata* (L.). *Journal of Natural History, 5*: 17-28. **S**

Kirby, P., & Lambert, S.J. 1990. A provisional list of the Heteroptera of Ceredigion (VC46). *Dyfed Invertebrate Group Newsletter, No. 17*: 1-9. **M**

Loxton, R.G. 1986. A pitfall trap study of habitat use by invertebrates on Ynys Enlli: 1. Coleoptera, Carabidae. *Bardsey Observatory Report, No. 30*: 41-69. **N**

Luff, M.L. 1987. Ground-beetles in Dyfed. *Dyfed Invertebrate Group Newsletter, No. 6*: 3-5. **M, S**

Luxton, M. 1967. The ecology of saltmarsh Acarina. *Journal of Animal Ecology, 36*: 257-277. **S**

McMillan, N.F., & Millott, J. O'N. 1949. Records of non-marine Mollusca from Cheshire, Flintshire and Denbighshire. *Cheshire and North Wales Natural History, 3*: 165-172. **N**

McMillan, N.F., & Millott, J. O'N. 1954. Notes on the non-marine Mollusca of Cheshire and North Wales. *Cheshire and North Wales Natural History, 5*: 109-113. **N**

Majerus, M. 1987. Ladybirds in Dyfed, 1985-1986. *Dyfed Invertebrate Group Newsletter, No. 5*: 3-7. **M, S**

Merrett, C.M. 1983. The spiders of Kenfig nature reserve. *Nature in Wales, 2*: 63-69. **S**

Michaelis, H.N. 1950. Records of Lepidoptera comprising the Pyralidina and Psychina found in the counties of Cheshire, Flintshire, Denbighshire, Caernarvonshire, Anglesey, Merionethshire, Montgomeryshire and Cardiganshire. *Cheshire and North Wales Natural History, 4*: 47-73. **N, M**

Michaelis, H.N. 1954. Lepidoptera Pyralidina and Psychina. *Cheshire and North Wales Natural History, 5*: 52-54. **N**

Michaelis, H.N. 1954. Lepidoptera. Tortricina. Records of species found in the counties of Cheshire, Flintshire, Denbighshire, Caernarvonshire, Anglesey, Merionethshire, Montgomeryshire and Cardiganshire. *Cheshire and North Wales Natural History, 5*: 55-90. **N, M**

Michaelis, H.N. 1969. Lepidoptera from the mountains of North Wales. *Nature in Wales, 11*: 183-191. **N**

Michaelis, H.N. 1971. The Lepidoptera of Coed Gorswen National Nature Reserve, Caernarvonshire. *Entomologist's Gazette, 22*: 65-95. **N**

Michaelis, H.N. 1977. The history and present status of *Luperina nickerlii gueneei* Doubleday in Britain. *Entomologist's Record and Journal of Variation, 89*: 183-185. **N**

Michaelis, H.N. 1977. Records of Gelechiidae (Lepidoptera) from North Wales. *Entomologist's Gazette, 28*: 217-222. **N**

Michaelis, H.N. 1981. Oecophoridae (Lep.) in Cheshire and North Wales. *Entomologists's Record and Journal of Variation, 93*: 60-65. **N**

Michaelis, H.N. 1983. Records of Coleophoridae (Lep.) in North Wales. *Entomologist's Record and Journal of Variation, 95*: 217-222. **N**

Michaelis, H.N. 1986. Species of Pyralidae and Pterophoridae (Lep.) in North Wales. *Entomologist's Record and Journal of Variation, 98*: 231-240. **N**

Morgan, I.K. 1986. Butterflies in Carmarthenshire. *West Wales Trust for Nature Conservation Bulletin,* No. 40: 7-8. **M, S**

Morgan, I.K. 1986. A checklist of the land molluscs of Carmarthenshire, VC44. *Dyfed Invertebrate Group Newsletter,* No. 2: 12-13. **M, S**

Morgan, I.K. 1988. Recent recording of Myriapods in south-west Wales. *Bulletin of the British Myriapod Group,* No. 5: 11-23. **M, S**

Morgan, I.K. 1990. Carmarthenshire Neuroptera. *Dyfed Invertebrate Group Newsletter,* No. 19: 6-8. **M, S**

Morgan, I.K. 1991. The millipedes of North Wales. *North Wales Invertebrate Group Newsletter,* No. 3: 4-6. **N**

Morgan, I.K. 1991. Carmarthenshire ladybirds. *Llanelli Naturalists Newsletter,* Summer 1991: 10-15. **M, S**

Morgan, M.J. 1965. The Lepidoptera of Caernarvonshire with special reference to the Bangor area. *Entomologist's Gazette, 16*: 43-80. **N**

Morgan, M.J. 1968. Thysanura in Caernarvonshire. *Entomologist, 101*: 73-75. **N**

Morgan, M.J. 1969. A check list of insects from

Bardsey Island, Caernarvonshire. *Entomologist's Gazette, 20*: 105-117. **N**

Morgan, M.J. 1974. Ashworth's rustic: a moth unique to Wales. *Nature in Wales, 14*: 117-121. **N**

Morgan, M.J. 1974. Coleoptera of Merioneth, North Wales: a supplement to Skidmore & Johnson's list, 1969. *Entomologist's Gazette, 25*: 53-75. **N**

Morgan, M.J. 1976. Neuroptera and Mecoptera in North Wales; a preliminary survey of their distribution. *Entomologist's Gazette, 27*: 229-247. **N**

Morgan, M.J. 1978. Mosquitoes in North Wales. *Nature in Wales, 16*: 102-104. **N**

Morgan, M.J. 1980. Microlepidoptera in Bangor. Notes on the species taken in a Rothamsted light-trap, 1966-1978. *Entomologist's Gazette, 31*: 23-36. **N**

Morgan, M.J. 1980. Asilidae (Dipt.) in North Wales. *Entomologist's Monthly Magazine, 116*: 123-125. **N**

Morgan, M.J. 1988. Microlepidoptera in Bangor. Species taken in a Rothamsted light-trap, 1979-1986. *Entomologist's Gazette, 39*: 141-149. **N**

Morris, D.L., & Brooker, M.P. 1979. The vertical distribution of macro-invertebrates in the substratum of the upper reaches of the River Wye, Wales. *Freshwater Biology, 9*: 573-583. **M**

Nelson, W. 1986. Damselflies of Glamorgan. *Gnat, 14*: 3-6. **S**

Norton, F. 1929. The Paraneuroptera of Glamorgan. *Transactions of the Cardiff Naturalists' Society, 62*: 73-75. **S**

Norton, F. 1933. The Ichneumonidae of Glamorgan. *Transactions of the Cardiff Naturalists' Society, 64*: 108-111. **S**

Owen, L. 1964. Spiders of the Gower sand dunes. *Gower, 16*: 6-10. **S**

O'Toole, C. 1973. A new subspecies of the vernal bee *Colletes cunicularius* (L.) (Hymenoptera: Colletidae). *Journal of Entomology (B), 42*: 163-169. **N**

Peers, M. 1985. The dragonflies of Radnorshire. *Flycatcher. Newsletter of the Herefordshire and Radnorshire Nature Trust,* No. 43: 30-36. **M**

Peers, M. 1985. The dragonflies of mid-Powys. *Journal of the British Dragonfly Society, 1*: 95-97. **M**

Piearce, T.G. 1972. A note on the earthworm fauna of North Wales. *Nature in Wales, 13*: 86-90. **N**

Popham, E.J. 1951. A short contribution towards an ecological survey of the aquatic and semi-aquatic Hemiptera-Heteroptera (water bugs) of the British Isles. North-east Wales (Denbighshire and Merionethshire). *Transactions of the Society for British Entomology, 10*: 269-280. **N**

Pyefinch, K.A. 1937. The fresh and brackish water of Bardsey Island (North Wales): a chemical and faunistic survey. *Journal of Animal Ecology, 6*: 115-137. **N**

Reynoldson, T.B. 1955. Observations on the earthworms of North Wales. *North Western Naturalist, N.S., 3*: 291-304. **N**

Reynoldson, T.B. 1958. The quantitative ecology of lake-dwelling triclads in northern Britain. *Oikos, 9*: 94-138. **N**

Reynoldson, T.B., & Jaques, R.M. 1976. Changes in the triclad (Turbellaria, Platyhelminthes) fauna of some North Wales lakes during the 20 years up to 1973. *Nature in Wales, 15*: 73-80. **N**

Sage, B.L. 1977. The Coleoptera of Skomer Island, Pembrokeshire, and their ecology. *Nature in Wales, 15*: 184-208. **M**

Sankey-Barker, J.P., Chalmers-Hunt, J.M., & Parker, H.G. 1978. *Butterflies and moths of Breconshire: a review of records.* Brecon, Brecknock Naturalists' Trust. **M**

Skidmore, P., & Johnson, C. 1969. A preliminary list of the Coleoptera of Merioneth, North Wales. *Entomologist's Gazette, 20*: 139-225. **N**

Smith, S.G. 1948. The butterflies and moths found in the counties of Cheshire, Flintshire, Denbighshire, Caernarvonshire, Anglesey and Merionethshire. *Cheshire and North Wales Natural History, 2*: 5-250. **N**

Smith, S.G. 1949. The butterflies and moths found in the county of Montgomeryshire and incorporating a supplement to the butterflies and moths of Cheshire, Flintshire, Denbighshire, Caernarvonshire, Anglesey and Merionethshire. *Proceedings of the Chester Society for Natural Science, Literature and Art, 2*: 1-250. **N, M**

Smith, S.G. 1954. The butterflies and moths found in the county of Radnorshire and incorporating

additional records of the butterflies and moths found in the counties of Cheshire, Flintshire, Denbighshire, Caernarvonshire, Anglesey, Merionethshire, Montgomeryshire and Cardiganshire. *Proceedings of the Chester Society for Natural Science, Literature and Art, 5*: 5-51. **N, M**

Staddon, B.W. 1961. The Plecoptera and Ephemeroptera of the Afon Lwyd and its tributaries in the eastern valley of Monmouthshire. *Entomologist's Monthly Magazine, 97*: 115-123. **S**

Thomas, C.D. 1985. Specialisations and polyphagy of *Plebejus argus* (Lepidoptera: Lycaenidae) in North Wales. *Ecological Entomology, 10*: 325-340. **N**

Thomas, C.D. 1985. The status and conservation of the butterfly *Plebejus argus* L. (Lepidoptera: Lycaenidae) in north west Britain. *Biological Conservation, 33*: 29-51. **N**

Tomlin, J.R. le B. 1912-1915. The Coleoptera of Glamorgan. *Transactions of the Cardiff Naturalists' Society, 45*: 41-58; *46*: 21-51; *47*: 13-33; *48*: 17-35. **S**

Tomlin, J.R. le B. 1933. Additions to the Coleoptera of Glamorgan. *Transactions of the Cardiff Naturalists' Society, 66*: 87-102. **S**

Wakefield, H.R. 1935. Breconshire Coleoptera. *Proceedings of the Swansea Scientific and Field Naturalist's Society, 1*: 271-285. **M**

Wistow, R.J. 1989. Dragonflies of the Montgomery Canal. *Journal of the British Dragonfly Society, 5*: 28-35. **M**

Appendix 4

Invertebrates occurring in Wales and protected by British &/or European legislation

	STATUS

CRUSTACEA
FRESHWATER CRAYFISH
Austropotamobius pallipes:
   WCA (Sch. 5) — taking & sale only.
   EC Directive (Annexes II & V).
	Local in clean rivers of eastern Wales.

FAIRY SHRIMP *Chirocephalus diaphanus*: WCA (Sch. 5).	Single site in Radnorshire.
MOLLUSCA WHORL SNAIL *Vertigo angustior*: EC Directive (Annex II).	Gower, two sites.

FRESHWATER PEARL MUSSEL
Margaritifera margaritifera:
   WCA (Sch. 5) — killing & injuring only.
   EC Directive (Annexes II & V).
	Status uncertain, still present in a few clean rivers.

GLUTINOUS SNAIL *Myxas glutinosa*: WCA (Sch. 5).	Llyn Tegid, probably extinct.

ANNELIDA
MEDICINAL LEECH
Hirudo medicinalis:
   WCA (Sch. 5).
   EC Directive (Annex V).
	Anglesey, 2 or 3 sites. Kenfig Pool, W. Glam.

INSECTA RAINBOW LEAF BEETLE *Chrysolina cerealis* WCA (Sch. 5).	Snowdonia only.
STAG BEETLE *Lucanus cervus* EC Directive (Annex II).	Occasional records from South Wales, status uncertain.
SOUTHERN DAMSELFLY *Coenagrion mercuriale* EC Directive (Annex II).	Anglesey, one site. Gower, two sites. Pembrokeshire, local.
WOOD WHITE *Leptidea sinapis* WCA (Sch. 5) — sale only.	Local in south and east Wales.
BROWN HAIRSTREAK *Thecla betulae* WCA (Sch. 5) — sale only.	Widespread in south-west Wales, uncommon elsewhere.
WHITE-LETTER HAIRSTREAK *Satyrium w-album* WCA (Sch. 5) — sale only.	Locally distributed throughout Wales.
SMALL BLUE *Cupido minimus* WCA (Sch. 5) — sale only.	Local along coast of South Wales and Dyfed.

SILVER-STUDDED BLUE
Plebejus argus   Scarce along coasts of North and South Wales, otherwise rare.
   WCA (Sch. 5) — salc only.
LARGE TORTOISESHELL
Nymphalis polychloros   Probably extinct as resident; occasional vagrants recorded.
   WCA (Sch. 5) — sale only.
PEARL-BORDERED FRITILLARY
Boloria euphrosyne   Scarce but widespread.
   WCA (Sch. 5) — sale only.
HIGH BROWN FRITILLARY
Argynnis adippe   Colonies in Mid Glamorgan and Powys, others unconfirmed.
   WCA (Sch. 5)
MARSH FRITILLARY
Eurodryas aurinia   Widespread in south and west Wales, few colonies elsewhere.
   WCA (Sch. 5) — sale only.
   EC Directive (Annex II).
LARGE HEATH
Coenonympha tullia   Scarce in North Wales and Cardiganshire.
   WCA (Sch. 5) — sale only.

NOTES:

WCA (Sch 5.)...Sixteen species of invertebrate occurring in Wales are listed on Schedule 5 of the Wildlife and Countryside Act 1981. Nine of these are butterflies for which, under the terms of Section 9 (5) of the Act, it is an offence to sell, or to offer for sale, live or dead specimens of any of the life stages. The freshwater (or Atlantic stream) crayfish is also protected from commercial exploitation and, in addition, is covered by part of Section 9 (1), such that the taking of specimens is an offence. The freshwater pearl mussel is given protection under Section 9 (1) such that it is an offence to intentionally kill or injure specimens. The remaining five species are given full protection under Section 9 of the Act, making it an offence to kill, injure, take, or sell live or dead specimens, or to disturb, damage or destroy their place of shelter or protection. A licence is necessary to carry out any of the proscribed activities to these species. Applications in respect of killing, injuring, taking or disturbing any species, or damaging or destroying its habitat, should be made to the Licensing Section, Countryside Council for Wales, Plas Penrhos, Ffordd Penrhos, Bangor, Gwynedd LL57 2LQ. Applications in respect of selling any species should be made to Wildlife Trading Licensing, Room 812, DoE, Tollgate House, Houlton Street, Bristol B52 9DJ.

EC Directive (Annexes II & V)...Council Directive 92/43/EEC of 21 May 1992 on the conservation of natural habitats and of wild fauna and flora (known as the EC Habitats Directive) lists seven species of invertebrate which occur in Wales. Annex II species are those "whose conservation requires the designation of special areas of conservation". Designated areas will be subject to detailed monitoring and management strategies to conserve and enhance populations of the relevant species. Three Welsh invertebrate species are included on Annex V. This applies to Article 14 of the Directive, which is designed to ensure that "their exploitation is compatible with their being maintained at a favourable conservation status". Each of these three species (medicinal leech, freshwater crayfish and freshwater pearl mussel) are already included on Schedule 5 of the Wildlife and Countryside Act.

General index

Index of localities

Index of invertebrate species